# Response to Marine Oil Spills

## 2nd Edition

**Witherby Seamanship International**
A Division of Witherby Publishing Group Ltd
4 Dunlop Square, Livingston, Edinburgh, EH54 8SB, Scotland, UK
Tel No: +44(0)1506 463 227 - Fax No: +44(0)1506 468 999
Email: info@emailws.com - Web: www.witherbyseamanship.com

First edition published 1986
Second edition published 2012

ISBN: 978-1-85609-354-5
eBook ISBN: 978-1-85609-506-8

**British Library Cataloguing in Publication Data**
A catalogue record for this book is available from the British Library.

Printed and bound in Great Britain by Bell & Bain Ltd, Glasgow

Published by

**Witherby Publishing Group Ltd**
4 Dunlop Square, Livingston,
Edinburgh, EH54 8SB,
Scotland, UK

Tel No: +44(0)1506 463 227
Fax No: +44(0)1506 468 999

Email: info@emailws.com
Web: www.witherbys.com

# Response to Marine Oil Spills

2nd Edition

# Content

# Introduction

## The International Tanker Owners Pollution Federation Ltd (ITOPF)

ITOPF is a not-for-profit organisation established on behalf of the world's shipowners and their insurers to promote effective response to marine spills of oil, chemicals and other hazardous substances. Technical services include emergency response, advice on clean-up techniques, damage assessment, claims analysis, assistance with spill response planning and the provision of training and information.

Since its establishment in 1968, ITOPF's technical staff have responded to several hundred shipping incidents worldwide to provide objective technical advice on clean-up measures, environmental and economic effects, and compensation. ITOPF has also provided remote advice at numerous other incidents. These incidents can involve crude oil from tankers, and bunker fuel, chemicals and bulk cargoes from all types of ship. Advice is also given occasionally in relation to oil spills from other potential sources of marine pollution, including pipelines and offshore installations, and physical damage to coral reefs resulting from ship groundings.

The first-hand experience gained by ITOPF's staff through direct involvement in pollution incidents is utilised during damage assessment, contingency planning and training assignments, as well as in the production of technical publications.

ITOPF's income is primarily through subscriptions from shipowners, paid via their Protection and Indemnity (P&I) insurers who enrol them in ITOPF as either Members or Associates. Enrolment allows access to a full range of technical and information services, usually at no cost.

ITOPF's membership comprises almost all the world's ocean going bulk oil, chemical and gas carrier tonnage. Associates comprise the owners and bareboat charterers of all other types of ship, reflecting ITOPF's important role in recent years in responding to bunker spills from non-tankers.

ITOPF's activities are overseen by an international Board of Directors representing the Federation's independent and oil company membership and their P&I insurers.

# SOURCES OF OIL IN THE MARINE ENVIRONMENT

**Worldwide Marine Waters**

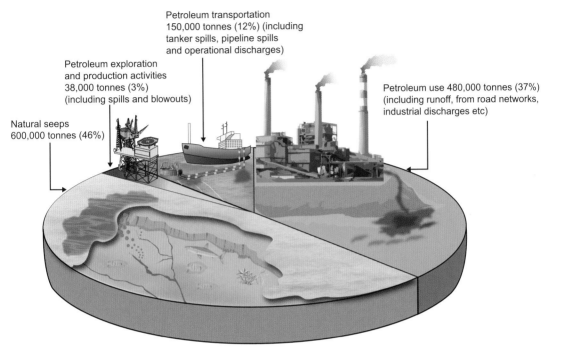

Petroleum transportation
150,000 tonnes (12%) (including
tanker spills, pipeline spills
and operational discharges)

Petroleum exploration
and production activities
38,000 tonnes (3%)
(including spills and blowouts)

Petroleum use 480,000 tonnes (37%)
(including runoff, from road networks,
industrial discharges etc)

Natural seeps
600,000 tonnes (46%)

■ **Figure 1.1: Average annual contribution to oil in the ocean (1990–1999). From 'Oil in the Sea III', National Academy of Sciences, USA**

 **Oil enters the sea from natural sources and through human activities. Inputs of oil into the marine environment are difficult to assess accurately on a global scale.**

In 2003, the National Academy of Sciences (USA) estimated that 1.3 million tonnes of oil entered the marine environment each year. Although oil in the ocean is commonly associated with tanker spills and oil rig blowouts, almost half (600,000 tonnes) of the total figure was estimated to be the result of natural seepage from geological formations beneath the seabed. 480,000 tonnes related to the use or consumption of refined products by, for example, cars, recreational boats, lawn mowers, jet skis, non-tank vessels and aeroplanes. This included runoff from urban roads, polluted rivers and storm and wastewater facilities, the improper disposal of used engine oil, spills and operational discharges from non-tank vessels and jettisoned aircraft fuel. The transportation of crude oil and refined products accounted for the release of an estimated 150,000 tonnes of oil into the sea each year, which made up just 12% of the total input. A further 38,000 tonnes, or 3%, was associated with offshore oil and gas activities.

While the amounts of oil discharged into the marine environment can fluctuate year upon year, the National Academy of Sciences study serves as a useful reminder of the variety of different sources from which it may come.

## 1.1 Transportation Losses

Transportation losses include tanker spills, pipeline spills, operational discharges from cargo washings, spills from coastal facilities such as refineries and emissions of volatile organic compounds (VOCs) during tanker operations. Releases due to the transportation of refined products make up roughly 12% of the annual total.

### 1.1.1 Accidental Spills from Tankers

Unlike chronic releases related to natural seepage or urban runoff, accidental spills from tankers can result in a sudden and significant quantity of oil entering the marine environment over a short period. Large spills can have severe environmental and economic effects, depending on a number of factors including the location of the spill, the characteristics of the affected area and the nature of the oil.

The ITOPF database contains information on approximately 10,000 oil spills from tankers, about 81% of which are less than 7 tonnes. The average number of large spills (>700 tonnes) during the 2000s was less than half of that for the 1990s and just an eighth of the average for the 1970s. This dramatic reduction has been due to the combined efforts of the tanker industry and governments (largely through the International Maritime Organization) to improve safety and pollution prevention.

The causes and circumstances of oil spills from tankers are varied, but can have a significant effect on the final quantity spilt. Small and medium sized spills (<7 tonnes and 7-700 tonnes respectively)

account for 95% of all the incidents recorded and a large proportion of them occurred during loading and discharging operations, which normally take place in ports and oil terminals. The remaining 5% of incidents comprise large spills, half of which occurred while the vessel was underway in open water. Allisions/collisions and groundings were the main cause of large spills, accounting for 62% of the total during the period 1974-2011. Other significant causes included hull failures and fire/explosion.

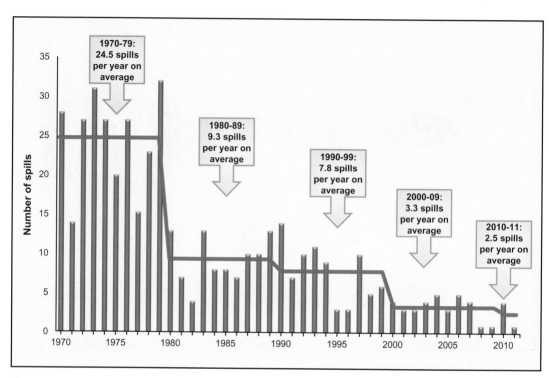

■ Figure 1.2: Number of large spills (over 700 tonnes), 1970-2011

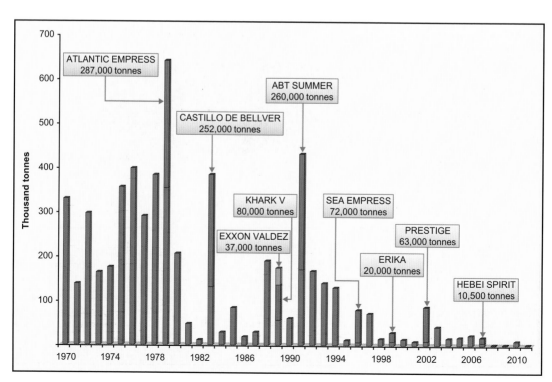

■ Figure 1.3: Quantities of oil spilt, 1970-2011

There is considerable annual variation in both the incidence of oil spills from tankers and the amounts of oil lost. It is notable that a few very large spills are responsible for a high percentage of the oil spilt. For example, in the ten-year period 2000-2009 there were 182 spills over 7 tonnes, totalling 212,000 tonnes, but 100,000 tonnes (47%) were spilt in just two incidents. The figures for a particular year may be severely distorted by a single large incident. This is clearly illustrated in 1979 (ATLANTIC EMPRESS - 287,000 tonnes, off Tobago, West Indies), 1983 (CASTILLO DE BELLVER - 252,000 tonnes, off Saldanha Bay, South Africa) and 1991 (ABT SUMMER - 260,000 tonnes, 700 nautical miles off Angola).

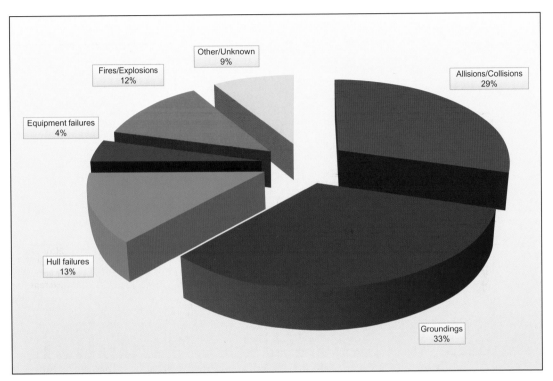

■ Figure 1.4: Causes of large spills (> 700 tonnes), 1974-2011

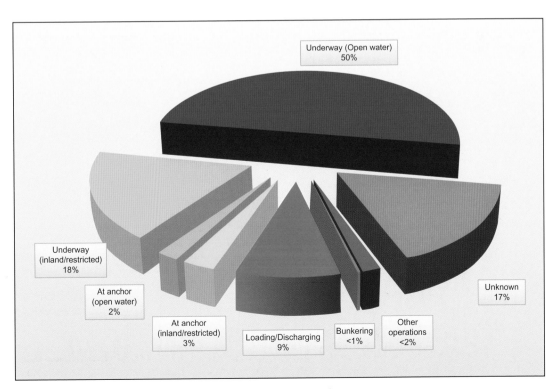

■ Figure 1.5: Operation at time of incident for large spills (>700 tonnes), 1974-2011

**ATLANTIC EMPRESS – off Tobago, West Indies, 1979**

On 19 July 1979, two fully loaded VLCCs (very large crude carriers), the ATLANTIC EMPRESS (288,000 dwt) and AEGEAN CAPTAIN (207,000 dwt), were involved in a collision approximately 10 miles off Tobago during a tropical rainstorm. Both vessels began leaking oil immediately after the collision and both caught fire. Several crewmen lost their lives.

The fire onboard the AEGEAN CAPTAIN was brought under control and the vessel was eventually towed to Curaçao, where its remaining cargo was discharged. The still blazing ATLANTIC EMPRESS was towed further out to sea on 21 and 22 July. A week later, when 300 nautical miles offshore, a large explosion caused severe damage to the vessel; it began to list and eventually sank on 2 August.

The response to the incident involved a significant fire-fighting effort and use of dispersants to treat the oil that was spilt during the original incident and while the vessel was being towed.

An estimated 287,000 tonnes of oil was spilt from the ATLANTIC EMPRESS, which makes this the largest ship source spill ever recorded. Only very minor shoreline pollution occurred on nearby islands and there were no reports of environmental damage.

### 1.1.2 Other Transportation Losses

Before international regulations were introduced, it was normal practice for oil tankers to wash out their cargo tanks with water and pump the resulting oil and water mix into the sea. Oil was also discharged when tankers flushed out dirty ballast water from cargo and fuel tanks. Operational discharges of oil from ships are still permitted but they are strictly regulated, most notably under the international convention MARPOL 73/78. Developments such as segregated ballast tank (SBT) arrangements, crude oil washing (COW) systems and load on top (LOT) procedures have led to a significant reduction in the amount of operational pollution from tankers.

Transportation losses also include discharges of fuel oil sludge and oily bilge water from machinery spaces. With proper equipment onboard, dirty bilge water can be processed in a way that separates most of the oil from the water before it is discharged into the sea. Although the quantities of waste oil discharged to the sea from ships can be controlled through strict management, adequate shore reception facilities for tanker slops and oily residues also play an important role.

On a smaller scale, pipeline spills, spills from coastal facilities and VOC emissions from tankers contribute to the inputs from transportation.

## 1.2 Petroleum Exploration and Production Activities

A large number of small releases occur during routine operations such as the discharge of produced water and the disposal of oil-based muds. Major pollution incidents from offshore activities, such as blowouts, are rare but can result in large volumes of oil being lost if the well is not brought under control quickly. A notable case is the exploratory well IXTOC I, which suffered a blowout on 3 June 1979, releasing at least 476,000 tonnes of oil into the Gulf of Mexico before it was capped on 24 March 1980. This was eclipsed in 2010 when a gas release and subsequent explosion occurred on the DEEPWATER HORIZON oil rig working on the Macondo exploration well for BP in the Gulf of Mexico. Eleven people died as a result of the accident and others were injured. The fire burned for 36 hours before the rig sank and oil leaked into the Gulf of Mexico for 87 days before the well was closed and sealed. Official estimates put the size of the spill at 4.9 million barrels (approximately 668,360 tonnes), making this the world's largest accidental release of oil. Such catastrophic events are uncommon however, and improved production technology and safety measures in recent years have significantly reduced the amount of oil lost through E&P related activities.

## 1.3 Petroleum Use

Major inputs of oil into the sea arise from the consumption of petroleum and include discharges of process water at coastal refineries and other industries, waste oil carried to the sea in sewage discharges and rivers, the use of recreational marine vessels, urban runoff from road networks, fuel dumps from aircraft and atmospheric inputs from manufacturing facilities, power plants and road vehicles.

## 1.4 Natural Seeps and Erosion

The largest contribution of oil into the marine environment is made by natural seeps in the seabed and the erosion of coastal land. Natural inputs are difficult to quantify and are unevenly distributed. Seeps tend to be associated with regions that have tectonic activity in oceanic margins, while erosion of exposed oil-rich sediments takes place in terrestrial locations and usually form part of the river runoff. Release rates are relatively low and chronic and the environmental impact is usually limited.

Spilt oil is eventually assimilated by the marine environment, but the time this takes will depend on factors such as:

- The quantity spilt
- initial physical and chemical characteristics
- climatic and marine conditions
- whether it remains at sea or is washed ashore.

Interaction of these factors will alter the nature, composition and behaviour of the oil over time, either leading to its natural dissipation or causing it to persist. An understanding of the processes involved is fundamental when deciding how to respond effectively to an oil spill at sea.

## 2.1 Properties of Oil

The main physical properties that affect the behaviour and the persistence of an oil spilt at sea are:

### Specific gravity (or relative density)
This is the density of an oil measured in relation to pure water. Most oils have a specific gravity below 1, making them lighter than sea water, which is about 1.025. The American Petroleum Institute (API) gravity scale, °API, is commonly used to describe the specific gravity of crude oils and petroleum products. It is calculated as follows:

$$°API = \frac{141.5}{Specific\ gravity} - 131.5$$

Specific gravity not only determines whether the oil will float but will also provide an indication of its other properties. For example, oils with a low specific gravity (high °API) tend to contain a high proportion of volatile components and to be of low viscosity. As a general rule, the lower the API, the heavier the oil.

### Distillation characteristics
These relate to the volatility of the oil. When the temperature of oil rises, different components gradually reach their boiling point and evaporate. The distillation characteristics are expressed as the proportions of the parent oil that distil within given temperature ranges. Some oils contain bituminous, waxy or asphaltenic residues, which even at high temperatures do not readily distil or evaporate. Oils such as these are likely to persist in the environment for extended periods.

### Viscosity
Viscosity determines an oil's resistance to flow. High viscosity oils do not flow as easily as those with lower viscosity. All oils become more viscous as their temperature falls, which is likely to happen soon after a spill as the temperature of sea water tends to be lower than cargo or bunker temperatures onboard a vessel. The efficiency of 'viscosity-dependent' clean-up operations, such as skimming and pumping, will be affected by high viscosity oils or by oil that is cooling.

### Pour point
This is the temperature below which an oil will not flow. As an oil cools it will reach a temperature at which the wax components begin to form crystalline structures, known as the 'cloud point'. This increasingly hinders the flow of the oil until it eventually changes from liquid to semi-solid at the pour point.

## 2.2 The Weathering Processes

Spilt oil is affected by physical and chemical changes that are collectively known as 'weathering'. There are eight different processes, several of which may occur simultaneously, but their relative importance will change over time.

The processes are illustrated in Figure 2.1, which shows them for a spill of a typical medium crude in moderate sea conditions.

As a general rule, each process can be put into one of two chronological categories:

- Early stage of a spill: spreading, evaporation, dispersion, emulsification and dissolution
- later stage of a spill: oxidation, sedimentation and biodegradation. These are longer term processes that will determine the ultimate fate of the oil spilt.

### Spreading
Spilt oil will immediately start to spread over the sea surface. The main driving force behind the initial spreading of the oil is its viscosity and volume.

A large instantaneous spill will spread more quickly than a slow discharge because of the weight behind it. Liquid oils will initially spread as a coherent slick that soon begins to break up, whereas solid or highly viscous oils tend to fragment into patches rather than spreading to thin layers.

■ **Oils spilt into the sea at temperatures below their pour point form solid fragments**

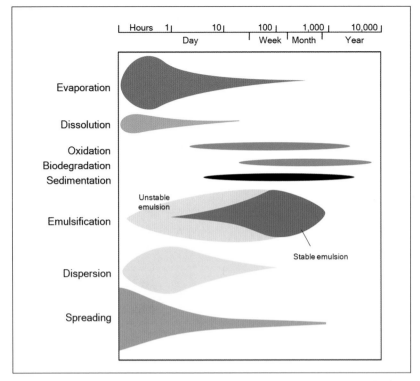

■ **Figure 2.1: A schematic representation of the fate of a typical Group 2 or 3 crude oil spill, showing changes in the relative importance of weathering processes with time. The width of each band indicates the importance of the process (after a diagram courtesy of SINTEF)**

|  | **Group 1** | **Group 2** | **Group 3** | **Group 4** |
|---|---|---|---|---|
|  | Arabian Super Light | Brent | Cabinda | Merey |
| Origin | Saudi Arabia | UK | Angola | Venezuela |
| °API | 50.7 | 37.9 | 32.5 | 17.3 |
| Specific gravity at 15°C | 0.79 | 0.83 | 0.86 | 0.96 |
| Wax content | 12% | No data | 10.4% | 10% |
| Asphaltenes | 7% | 0.5 | 0.16 | 9% |
| Pour point | −39°C | −3°C | 12°C | −21°C |

■ **Table 2.1: Physical characteristics of four typical crude oils. The group numbers correspond to the classification in Table 2.2**

It should be noted that, except in the case of small spills of low viscosity oils, spreading is not uniform and large variations of oil thickness can occur. If the temperature falls below the oil's pour point it will rapidly solidify and spreading will be greatly reduced. In this circumstance the oil may remain up to several centimetres thick.

Further spreading will be dictated by winds, wave action and water turbulence, which can cause oil to form narrow bands, or 'windrows', parallel to the wind direction. The more severe the conditions the more rapid the spreading and breaking up of the oil. Tidal streams and currents also affect the rate at which oil spreads or fragments.

It is not uncommon for oil spills to spread over several square kilometres in a few hours, and over several hundreds of square kilometres within a few days, seriously limiting the possibility of effective clean-up at sea.

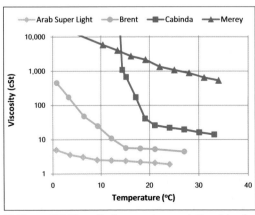

■ **Figure 2.2: Viscosity/temperature relationship for the crude oils in Table 2.1**

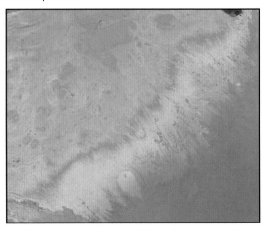

■ **When medium and light oils spread unhindered, they eventually form very thin films or 'sheen'**

## Evaporation

The rate and extent of evaporation is determined by several factors:

- Volatility
- ambient temperature
- wind speed
- initial spreading rate.

An oil with a high percentage of light and volatile compounds will evaporate more than one with a larger amount of heavier compounds. For example, gasoline, kerosene and diesel oils are all light products and may evaporate completely within a few hours. Light crudes can lose up to 40% of their volume during the first day. In contrast, there is little, if any, evaporation from heavy fuel oils.

When extremely volatile oils are spilt in a confined area there may also be a risk of fire and explosion or there could be human health hazards.

The initial spreading rate of the oil spilt affects evaporation because the light components will evaporate faster when the surface area is large. Rough seas, high wind speeds and warm temperatures will also increase the rate of evaporation. Any residue of oil remaining after evaporation will have an increased density and viscosity, which affects subsequent weathering processes and the effectiveness of clean-up techniques.

## Dispersion

Waves and turbulence at the sea surface can cause all or part of a slick to break up into droplets of varying sizes, which will start dispersing through the water column.

Smaller droplets tend to remain in suspension aided by the turbulent motion of the sea, which mixes the oil into ever greater volumes of sea water. The larger droplets will rise back to the surface, where they either coalesce with other droplets to reform a slick or spread out in a very thin film, often referred to as 'sheen'. The oil that remains suspended in the water has a greater surface area after dispersion, which encourages other natural processes such as dissolution, biodegradation and sedimentation.

The natural rate of dispersion largely depends on the nature of the oil and the sea state:

- Low viscosity oils, in the presence of breaking waves, will be the fastest to disperse and may disperse completely within a few days. These factors led to the complete dispersion of the oil spilt from the BRAER (Shetland, UK, 1993). The application of dispersants can speed up the process of dispersion

- viscous oils and oils at temperatures below their pour point tend to form thick fragments on the water surface that show little tendency to disperse, even with the addition of dispersants. These oils can persist for weeks and, on reaching the shore, they may eventually form hard asphalt pavements if not removed.

### BRAER – Shetland, UK, 1993

Following engine failure, the oil tanker BRAER ran aground in severe weather conditions on Garth's Ness, Shetland, on 5 January 1993. Over a period of 12 days the entire cargo of 84,700 tonnes of Norwegian Gullfaks crude oil, plus up to 1,500 tonnes of heavy bunker oil, were lost as almost constant storm force winds and heavy seas broke the ship apart. Weather conditions prevented the use of mechanical recovery equipment at sea, although about 130 tonnes of dispersant was applied from aircraft during periods when the wind abated slightly and some oil remained on the surface. Oiling of shorelines was minimal relative to the size of the spill and clean-up involved the collection of oily debris and seaweed by a small workforce.

The BRAER spill was very unusual in that a surface slick was not produced. A combination of the light nature of the oil and the exceptionally strong wind and wave energy naturally dispersed the oil throughout the water column. The oil droplets were adsorbed onto sediment particles that eventually sank to the seabed. Subsurface currents led to this oil being spread over a very wide area, although a significant proportion eventually ended up in two deep, fine sediment 'sinks'.

A wide range of fish and shellfish over a fairly large area became contaminated with oil, resulting in the imposition of a Fisheries Exclusion Zone. Farmed salmon held in sea cages in the surface waters within this zone bore the brunt of the contamination as they could not escape the cloud of dispersed oil. Although this contamination was lost quickly once clean water conditions returned, salmon that could not be marketed had to be destroyed. The Exclusion Zone was progressively lifted as fish and shellfish species were found by chemical analysis and taint testing to be free of contamination.

The Exclusion Zone was still in place for mussels and Norway lobsters at some sites within the closure area over 6 years after the spill.

Another unusual feature of the BRAER incident was that a significant amount of oil was blown onto land adjacent to the wreck site. The effects of this airborne oil were localised and had no more than a temporary impact on vegetation and livestock. Seabird casualties were also relatively low due to the storm conditions and the oil's disappearance from the sea surface. There was little, if any, sea mammal mortality.

The BRAER ranks as one of the world's largest oil spills, spilling more than twice as much as the EXXON VALDEZ, but its environmental impact was surprisingly limited. The oil's thorough dispersion into the water column mimimised the damage a surface slick would have caused, but provided a route by which significant quantities of oil were deposited onto the seabed. No major impacts on the seabed communities were recorded, however, suggesting that the BRAER oil was of overall low toxicity.

## Emulsification

In moderate to rough seas, most oils will absorb water droplets under the turbulent action of waves on the sea surface. The resulting 'water-in-oil emulsion' can increase the volume of pollutant by up to 5 times and is usually very viscous and more persistent than the original oil.

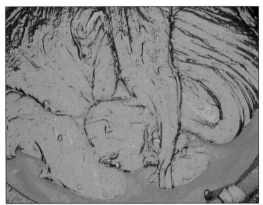

■ **Water-in-oil emulsion**

Emulsions will form most readily and rapidly when:

- The fresh oil has a combined nickel/vanadium concentration greater than 15 ppm or an asphaltene content in excess of 0.5%

- the sea state is greater than Beaufort Force 3 (wind speed 4-5 ms$^{-1}$ (7-10 knots)). In these conditions low viscosity oils can incorporate up to 75% of water within a few hours

- the spilt oil has low viscosity. Very viscous oils, such as heavy fuel oils, tend to take up water more slowly than more liquid oils and will seldom, even after several days, contain more than 40% of water.

As the emulsion develops the movement of the oil in waves causes the droplets of water captured in the oil to become smaller, causing the emulsion to become progressively more viscous and stable.

Stable emulsions, sometimes referred to as 'chocolate mousse' because of their appearance, are often semi-solid with a brown, orange or yellow colour. They are highly persistent and may remain emulsified indefinitely. Less stable emulsions may separate out into oil and water if heated by sunlight under calm conditions or when stranded on shorelines.

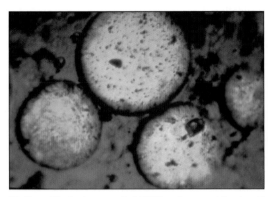

■ **Magnified image (×1,000) of a water-in-oil emulsion, showing individual water droplets surrounded by oil**

Emulsification slows and delays other processes that would allow the oil to dissipate and is the main reason for the persistence of light and medium crude oils on the sea surface.

■ **Water in oil emulsions often accumulate on shores in thick layers**

## Dissolution

Water soluble compounds in an oil may dissolve into the surrounding water. This depends on the composition and state of the oil, and occurs most quickly when the oil is finely dispersed in the water column. Components that are most soluble in sea water are the light aromatic hydrocarbons, such as benzene and toluene. However, these compounds are also the first to be lost through evaporation, a process that is 10-1000 times faster than dissolution. Oil contains only small amounts of these compounds, making dissolution one of the less important weathering processes.

## Oxidation

Oils can react with oxygen, leading to the formation of either soluble products or persistent compounds called tars.

Oxidation is promoted by sunlight and, although it occurs throughout the existence of a slick, its overall effect on dissipation is minor. Even under intense sunlight thin oil films break down slowly, at no more than 0.1% per day. Thick layers of high viscosity oils or emulsions tend to oxidise to persistent residues rather than degrade, as heavy compounds are formed that create a protective surface layer. Tarballs, which are often found on shorelines and have a solid outer crust surrounding a softer, less weathered interior, are a typical example of this process.

## Sedimentation

Some heavy refined products have specific gravities greater than sea water (1.025), causing them to sink in fresh or brackish water. Most crude and fuel oils have sufficiently low specific gravities to remain afloat unless they interact with and attach to more dense sediment or organic particles.

Temperature variations will also have an impact. Over a 10°C temperature range the density of sea water will change by only 0.25%, while oil density will change by 0.5%. Consequently, oil that barely floats during the day may submerge at night when the temperature drops, resurfacing when the water warms up again.

Planktonic organisms may also ingest oil, which then becomes incorporated into faecal pellets that will eventually fall to the seabed.

In addition, if the oil catches fire after it has spilt, the residues that sometimes form can be dense enough to sink.

Sedimentation is most likely to take place in shallow waters, when oils strand or become buried on beaches, such as in the circumstances described below:

- Coastal areas, rivermouth waters and estuaries are often laden with suspended solids that can bind with dispersed oil droplets, providing favourable conditions for sedimentation of oily particles to the seabed. Fresh water from rivers also lowers the salinity and specific gravity of sea water, encouraging neutrally buoyant droplets to sink

- on exposed beaches, heavy contamination may lead to an accumulation of large amounts of sediment in the oil, forming dense 'tar mats'. Seasonal cycles of sediment build-up and erosion may cause oil layers to be successively buried and uncovered. If washed back out to sea by storms, tides or currents, the oil mixed with beach sediment will sink

- on sheltered shorelines, where wave action and currents are weak, muddy sediments and marshes are common. If oil becomes incorporated into such fine grained sediments it is likely to remain there for a considerable time.

Oil droplets in the water column can adhere to very fine mineral particles to form flocculates, which may be widely dispersed by currents or turbulence. Storms, turbulence or tidal rise and fall can also encourage the small quantities of oil in seabed sediments or on beaches to be attached to such particles may become suspended in the water. This process, sometimes referred to as clay-oil flocculation, can gradually remove oil from beaches over a period of time.

■ **When oil is mixed with sediment the density can become high enough for it to sink if it is washed off the beach**

## Biodegradation

Sea water contains a range of marine microorganisms, including bacteria, moulds, yeasts, fungi, unicellular algae and protozoa, which partially or completely degrade oil to water soluble compounds, and eventually to carbon dioxide and water. These organisms live in all waters, but are most abundant in chronically polluted coastal areas that experience busy vessel traffic or receive industrial discharges and untreated sewage. While these biodegrading organisms are present in only small numbers in the open sea, they will rapidly multiply when oil is available.

The main factors affecting the rate and extent of biodegradation are:

- The characteristics of the oil

- the availability of oxygen in the water

- the availability of nutrients in the water (principally compounds of nitrogen and phosphorus)

- the water temperature.

A wide range of microorganisms will work together or in succession to complete the degradation process as each different type feeds on a specific group of hydrocarbons. Consequently, as degradation proceeds, a complex community of microorganisms will develop. Most of the compounds in crude oil can be disintegrated by biodegradation, but some large and complex molecules will remain resistant to attack.

As biodegradation requires oxygen, this process can only take place at the oil-water interface as no oxygen is available within the oil itself. The creation of oil droplets, either by natural or chemical dispersion, increases the interfacial area available for biological activity and so may enhance biodegradation.

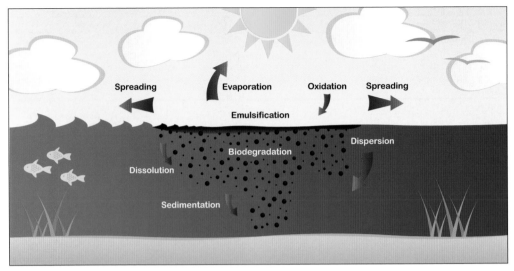

■ **Figure 2.3: Weathering processes acting on oil at sea**

Oil stranded in thick layers on shorelines or above the high water mark will have a limited surface area and will be subject to drier conditions, which will make degradation extremely slow, resulting in the oil persisting for many years. Once oils become incorporated into sediments on the shoreline or seabed, degradation is very much reduced or may stop through a lack of oxygen and/or nutrients.

The variety of the factors that influence biodegradation makes it difficult to predict the rate at which oil may disappear. In temperate waters daily degradation rates of between 0.001–0.03 grams per tonne of sea water have been reported, but the figure may reach up to 60 grams in areas of chronic oil pollution.

Although biodegradation is a slow process and will not remove bulk oil accumulations, it is one of the main mechanisms through which dispersed oil or final traces of a shoreline spill are eventually removed.

 An understanding of the way in which weathering processes interact is important when attempting to forecast the changing characteristics of an oil slick during its lifetime at sea and its likely persistence in the marine environment.

## 2.3 Persistence of Oil

When considering the fate of spilt oil at sea, a distinction is frequently made between persistent and non-persistent oils as this allows a quick assessment of the most appropriate response options.

Non-persistent oils, because of their volatile nature and low viscosity, will disappear more rapidly, while persistent oils dissipate more slowly and usually require a clean-up response. Non-persistent oils include gasoline, naphtha and kerosene, while the persistent group includes most crude oils, heavy fuel oils and bitumens.

For more accurate predictions of persistence, classification of oils into four main groups, according to their °API or specific gravity, is helpful (see Table 2.2). Group I oils (non-persistent) tend to

dissipate completely through evaporation within a few hours and do not normally form emulsions. Group 2 and 3 oils can lose up to 40% by volume through evaporation but, because of their tendency to form viscous emulsions, there is an initial volume increase as well as a curtailment of natural dispersion, particularly in the case of Group 3 oils. Group 4 oils are very persistent due to their lack of volatile material and high viscosity, which preclude both evaporation and dispersion. They include the heavy fuel oils that are carried as bunker fuel by many ships and are among the most problematic to clean-up. Their persistence gives them the potential to travel considerable distances at sea and cause widespread contamination.

 As a general rule, the higher the °API of the oil (and the lower the specific gravity), the less persistent it will be.

It is important to note that some apparently light oils can behave more like heavy ones due to the presence of waxes. Oils with a wax content greater than about 10% tend to have high pour points and, if the ambient temperature is low, the oil will either be a semi-solid or a highly viscous liquid and the natural weathering processes will be slow.

Figure 2.4 shows, for Groups 2-4, typical increases in viscosity with time after spillage as a result of evaporation and emulsification, demonstrating that emulsification has the largest effect on the increase in viscosity.

Figure 2.5 shows a simplified schematic of the rate of natural removal of the four oil groups and also takes into account the effect of the formation of water-in-oil emulsions on the volume of oil over time. The schematic has been developed on the basis of observations made in the field and provides a general impression of how persistence varies according to the physical properties of the oil. In reality, weather and climatic conditions will also influence the persistence of a slick. For example, in very rough weather an oil in Group 3 may dissipate within a timescale more typical of a Group 2 oil. Conversely, in cold, calm conditions it may approach the persistence of the Group 4 oils.

## Group 1 oils

A: °API > 45 (Specific gravity < 0.8)
B: Pour point °C:
C: Viscosity @ 10–20°C: less than 3 CSt
D: % boiling below 200°C: greater than 50%
E: % boiling above 370°C: between 20 and 0%

|  | A | B | C | D | E |
|---|---|---|---|---|---|
| Aasgard | 49 | -28 | 2 @ 10°C | 58 | 14 |
| Arabian Super Light | 51 | -39 | 2 @ 20°C |  |  |
| Cossack | 48 | -18 | 2 @ 20°C | 51 | 18 |
| Curlew | 47 | -13 | 2 @ 20°C | 57 | 17 |
| F3 Condensate | 54 | <-63 | 1 @ 10°C | 81 | 0 |
| Gippsland | 52 | -13 | 1.5 @ 20°C | 63 | 8 |
| Hidra | 52 | -62 | 2.5 @ 10°C | 60 | 11 |
| Terengganu condensate | 73 | -36 | 0.5 @ 20°C | >95 | 0 |
| Wollybutt | 49 | -53 | 2@ 20°C | 55 | 4 |
| Gasoline | 58 |  | 0.5 @ 15°C | 100 | 0 |
| Kerosene | 45 | -55 | 2 @ 15°C | 50 | 0 |
| Naptha | 55 |  | 0.5 @ 15°C | 100 | 0 |

## Group 2 oils

A: °API 35 – 45 (Specific gravity 0.8–0.85)
B: Pour point °C:
C: Viscosity @ 10–20°C: between 4 Cst and semi-solid
D: % boiling below 200°C: between 20 and 50%.
E: % boiling above 370°C: between 15 and 50%.

| Low pour point <6°C | A | B | C | D | E |
|---|---|---|---|---|---|
| Arabian Extra Light | 38 | -30 | 3 @ 15°C | 26 | 39 |
| Azeri | 37 | -3 | 8 @ 20°C | 29 | 46 |
| Brent | 38 | -3 | 7 @ 10°C | 37 | 33 |
| Draugen | 40 | -15 | 4 @ 20°C | 37 | 32 |
| Dukhan | 41 | -49 | 9 @ 15°C | 36 | 33 |
| Liverpool Bay | 45 | -21 | 4 @ 20°C | 42 | 28 |
| Sokol (Sakhalin) | 37 | -27 | 4 @ 20°C | 45 | 21 |
| Rio Negro | 35 | -5 | 23 @ 10°C | 29 | 41 |
| Umm Shaif | 37 | -24 | 10 @ 10C | 34 | 31 |
| Zakum | 40 | -24 | 6@ 10°C | 36 | 33 |
| Marine Gas oil (MGO) | 37 | -3 | 5 @ 15°C |  |  |
| High pour point >5°C | A | B | C | D | E |
| Amna | 36 | 19 | Semi–solid | 25 | 30 |
| Beatrice | 38 | 18 | 32 @ 15°C | 25 | 35 |
| Bintulu | 37 | 19 | Semi–solid | 24 | 34 |
| Escravos | 34 | 10 | 9 @ 15°C | 35 | 15 |
| Sarir | 38 | 24 | Semi–solid | 24 | 39 |
| Statfjord | 40 | 6 | 7 @ 10°C | 38 | 32 |

Note: High pour point oils only behave as Group 2 at ambient temperatures above their pour point. Below this treat as Group 4 oils.

## Group 3 oils

A: °API 17.5–35 (Specific gravity 0.85–0.95)
B: Pour point °C:
C: Viscosity @ 10–20°C: between 8 CSt and semi solid
D: % boiling below 200°C: between 10 and 35%.
E: % boiling above 370°C: between 30 and 65%.

| Low pour point <6°C | A | B | C | D | E |
|---|---|---|---|---|---|
| Alaska North Slope | 28 | -18 | 32 @ 15°C | 32 | 41 |
| Arabian Heavy | 28 | -40 | 55 @ 15°C | 21 | 56 |
| Arabian Medium | 30 | -21 | 25 @ 15°C | 22 | 51 |
| Arabian Light | 33 | -40 | 14 @ 15°C | 25 | 45 |
| Bonny Light | 35 | -11 | 25 @ 15°C | 26 | 30 |
| Iranian Heavy | 31 | -36 | 25 @ 15°C | 24 | 48 |
| Iranian Light | 34 | -32 | 15 @ 15°C | 26 | 43 |
| Khafji | 28 | -57 | 80 @ 15°C | 21 | 55 |
| Sirri | 33 | -12 | 18 @ 10°C | 32 | 38 |
| Thunder Horse | 35 | -27 | 10 @ 10°C | 32 | 39 |
| Tia Juana Light | 32 | -42 | 500 @ 15°C | 24 | 45 |
| Troll | 33 | -9 | 14 @ 10°C | 24 | 35 |
| IFO 180 | 18–20 | 10-30 | 1,500-3,000 @ 15°C | - |  |
| High pour point >5°C | A | B | C | D | E |
| Cabinda | 33 | 12 | Semi–solid | 18 | 56 |
| Coco | 32 | 21 | Semi–solid | 21 | 46 |
| Gamba | 31 | 23 | Semi–solid | 11 | 54 |
| Mandji | 30 | 9 | 70 @ 15°C | 21 | 53 |
| Minas | 35 | 18 | Semi–solid | 15 | 58 |

Note: High pour point oils only behave as Group 3 at ambient temperatures above their pour point. Below this treat as Group 4 oils.

## Group 4 oils

A: °API <17.5 (Specific gravity >0.95) or B: Pour point >30°C
C: Viscosity @ 10–20°C: between 1500 CSt and semi-solid
D: % boiling below 200°C: less than 25%
E: % boiling above 370°C: greater than 30%

|  | A | B | C | D | E |
|---|---|---|---|---|---|
| Bachaquero 17 | 16 | -29 | 5000 @ 15°C | 10 | 60 |
| Boscan | 10 | 15 | Semi–solid | 4 | 80 |
| Cinta | 33 | 43 | Semi–solid | 10 | 54 |
| Handil | 33 | 35 | Semi–solid | 23 | 33 |
| Merey | 17 | -21 | 7,000 @ 15°C | 7 | 70 |
| Nile Blend | 34 | 33 | Semi–solid | 13 | 59 |
| Pilon | 14 | -3 | Semi–solid | 2 | 92 |
| Shengli | 24 | 21 | Semi–solid | 9 | 70 |
| Taching | 31 | 35 | Semi–solid | 12 | 49 |
| Tia Juana Pesado | 12 | -1 | Semi–solid | 3 | 78 |
| Widuri | 33 | 46 | Semi–solid | 7 | 70 |
| IFO 380 | 11–15 | 10–30 | 5,000 - 30,000 @ 15°C |  |  |

■ Table 2.2: Example oils classified according to their specific gravity. Indicative ranges of expected viscosities and distillation characteristics are provided for each group. Generally, persistence when spilt increases with group number

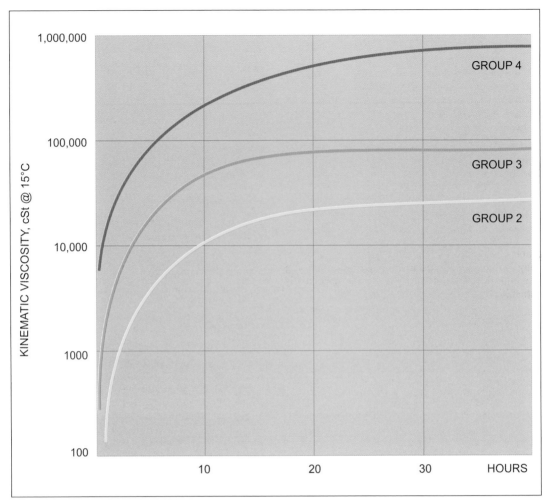

■ Figure 2.4: Typical rates of viscosity increase in moderate to heavy seas. The viscosity of Group 1 oils never exceeds 100 cSt in the marine environment and so is not shown

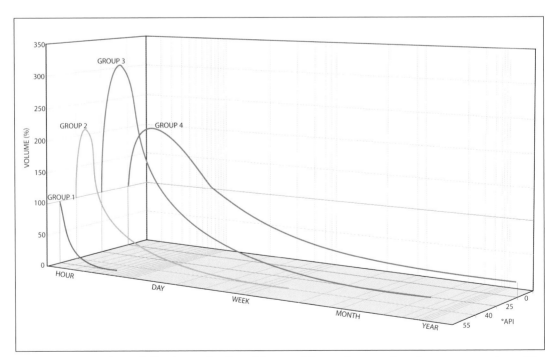

■ Figure 2.5: The volume of oil and water-in-oil emulsion remaining on the sea surface shown as a percentage of the original spill volume (100%). The curve represents an estimated 'average' behaviour for each group. However, the behaviour of a particular crude oil may differ from the general pattern, depending on its properties and the environmental conditions at the time of the spill

## 2.4 Forecasting Slick Movement and Weathering

It is important to be able forecast the probable movement of a slick as well as the likely changes in the properties of an oil after it has been spilt. This allows sensitive resources in the path of the slick to be identified and, if appropriate, response measures to be put into effect.

The mechanisms governing spill movement are complex, but a simple vector calculation of wind and surface current direction, based on about 3% of the wind speed and 100% of the current velocity, can be used to predict oil drift rate and direction. Reliability of this prediction will depend on the availability of accurate wind and current data, which can be difficult to obtain. For example, in shallow waters near a coast or among islands, currents may be complex and poorly understood, rendering accurate prediction of slick movement particularly difficult.

Weathering models that attempt to predict how a spilt oil will change with time under given sets of conditions have been developed. These often draw on databases of the physical and chemical characteristics of different oils, as well as the results of scientific research and observations of oil behaviour.

Weathering models can be combined with trajectory calculations to forecast the overall fate and potential impact of a slick.

It is important, however, to appreciate the assumptions upon which models are based and not place complete reliance on the results.

Models are widely used for contingency planning, where they are particularly helpful for decision makers who need to link their site-specific, pre-identified risks with decisions concerning the locations and planned response measures, including equipment, materials and manpower. This can be achieved by running the model several times, using a range of the most likely scenarios, and then observing the predicted oil movement and behaviour. Based on the results, those locations shown to be the most vulnerable can be identified, the logistics of responding to them studied, and response assets placed accordingly. There is, of course, no guarantee that these resources will be in the right place in the event of a spill, but the planners will have made the best judgement based on information available.

Spill response training is another key application of models. Trainers use the models in a variety of ways, but one approach is to run the model at real-time speed for 20-30 minutes so that participants can make some decisions about what measures should be taken and what equipment should be mobilised. Then the model is fast-forwarded to a later period and participants are asked to deal with the updated situation. In this way, an event of 2-3 days can be compressed into an hour or so.

The use of models in emergency response itself is more challenging, because it requires the timely acquisition of the numerous input parameters. In the initial stages of an incident, little may be known about the oil types or the quantities involved. As the incident develops better information will improve the output of the model.

**In response situations, model predictions should be verified by observations of actual oil distribution and behaviour.**

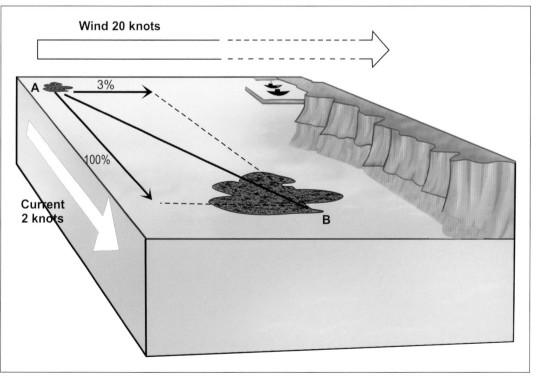

**Wind 20 knots**

A  3%

100%

Current 2 knots

B

■ **Figure 2.6: The influence of 3% of the wind speed, combined with 100% of the current speed, results in the movement of oil from A to B**

Nevertheless, models can provide a useful method of evaluating the clean-up techniques likely to be effective, for how long and with what problems. One immediate application is to inform decisions on the scope of initial aerial surveillance flights where the movement of oil may not be immediately obvious. Following an instantaneous release of oil at night, for example, the oil may have moved a considerable distance from the source.

Perhaps the most controversial application of modelling is for damage assessment. In the simplest cases, reference is made, for example, to the threshold levels of contaminants in marine products for safe human consumption. The geographic areas simulated as having been exposed to levels in excess of these standards are assumed to have been impacted. In more sophisticated models, input data for related toxicological studies is used together with ecological sub-models to predict what sort of acute exposure and impact may have been experienced. The problem with this approach is that the models do not actually show damage, they simply predict it based on a host of simplifying assumptions. Many years of field experience have made it clear that when there is significant impact, it can be observed on site.

## 2.5 Implications for Clean-up and Contingency Planning

**An understanding of the likely fate and behaviour of oil allows response techniques to be optimised and is key to effective contingency planning.**

The movement of slicks and the changing nature of the oil due to weathering can determine whether a response, beyond monitoring slick dissipation, is necessary at all. The tendency of oil to spread rapidly and fragment, particularly in rough sea conditions, will always place constraints on the effectiveness of any response option and should not be underestimated. Oil recovery systems, such as skimmers, typically have a swath width of only a few metres, rendering them largely inefficient once oil is scattered over many square kilometres of sea surface. For low viscosity oils this can happen in just a few hours and is the main reason why response at sea rarely results in the removal of much more than a fraction of a widely spread slick.

Where a response is called for, clean-up techniques will need to be re-evaluated and modified over time

as weathering processes can change an oil from a liquid to a semi-solid or solid state. For example, dispersants applied at sea reduce in efficiency as the oil spreads and as oil viscosity increases. Oil viscosity can increase quickly, making the time available for using dispersants very short. The effectiveness of the dispersant application should, therefore, be checked frequently. Similarly, if collection methods are employed, the type of pumps or skimmers used may need to be changed as the oil weathers and the viscosity increases.

■ **High oil viscosity has resulted in unsuccessful dispersant application, evidenced by the white plume of dispersant around the oil**

Understanding the likely fate and behaviour of different oils, and the constraint that this imposes on clean-up operations, is fundamental to preparing effective contingency plans. Information on the prevailing winds and currents throughout the year will help to indicate the most likely direction and rate of movement of the oil. Data on the types of oil handled and transported can enable predictions of the probable lifetime of slicks and the quantity and nature of the residue to be made. It will also determine the selection of appropriate clean-up techniques and types of equipment. For fixed installations, such as oil terminals and offshore oil fields, where a limited number of oil types are involved and prevailing conditions are well known, fairly accurate predictions can be made that simplify the development of an effective plan. Plans for areas where a wide range of oil types are handled or where tankers pass in transit cannot cover all eventualities. It is, therefore, very important that the type of oil spilt in an incident is established at the earliest opportunity.

# AERIAL SURVEILLANCE AT SEA 3

The fate and movement of oil slicks at sea should be verified through regular surveillance.

Attempting to view an oil spill from a vessel is rarely effective because of the limited height of the observation platform. By contrast, aerial reconnaissance provides an excellent way of determining the location and extent of oil contamination.

Aerial surveillance provides information that facilitates:

- The deployment and control of operations at sea
- the protection of sensitive sites along threatened coastlines
- the preparation of resources for shoreline clean-up.

**At the outset of an incident, reports from reconnaissance flights are often vital to establish the nature and scale of the pollution.**

Following initial mobilisation, subsequent fights should be made regularly. These are commonly timed at the beginning or end of each day so that the results can be used at decision meetings to plan response operations.

■ **Use of aircraft allows a rapid understanding of the spread of floating oil and the effectiveness of any response**

## 3.1 Preparations for Aerial Surveillance

### Safety considerations
Those taking part in a flight should be thoroughly briefed on the safety features of the aircraft and the procedures to be followed in the event of an emergency. Suitable personal protective equipment, such as life jackets, should be available and used.

### Choosing the aircraft
Consideration must be given to the location of the spill, the nearest airstrip and refuelling stations and the likely extent of sea and coastline to be included in a reconnaissance flight. Any aircraft used for aerial observation must feature good all-round visibility and carry suitable navigational aids. For example, if there is a choice of aircraft design, better visibility is afforded by high-mounted wings. Over near-shore waters the flexibility of helicopters is an advantage, particularly when surveying an intricate coastline with cliffs, coves and islands. However, over the open sea there is less need for rapid changes in flying speed, direction and altitude so the speed and range of fixed-wing aircraft are more advantageous. Aircraft selection should take operating speed into account as, if this is too fast, the ability to observe and record oil will be reduced. If it is too slow the flying distance will be limited. For surveys over the open sea the extra margin of safety afforded by a twin or multi-engined aircraft is essential and may be required by government regulations.

### Onboard observers
The number of observers onboard will depend on the type and size of the aircraft selected. It is important to note that, for small aircraft and helicopters in particular, the number of passengers can substantially affect fuel consumption and, therefore, the endurance of the aircraft. If there are two or more observers on a surveillance flight they should work closely together to compare and confirm sightings. The lead observer directing the pilot should be experienced in aerial surveillance and able to detect, recognise and record oil pollution at sea reliably. There should be consistency of at least one observer throughout a series of flights, so that variations in reports reflect changes in the state of oil pollution and not differences between the perceptions of the observers.

### Flight plan
A flight plan should be prepared in advance, taking account of any available information that may focus the search area. It should also take account of any flight restrictions, some of which may be specifically imposed as a result of the spill. For example, it may be prohibited to fly over the shipping casualty, foreign or military airspace or certain environmentally sensitive areas where wildlife, such as breeding colonies of birds or seals, may be disturbed. Due attention must also be paid to visibility and altitude, the likely flight duration and fuel availability.

A working plan should be prepared using extracts or copies of maps and charts of an appropriate scale to allow annotations to be made. Some basic data may usefully be included, such as latitude and longitude, the location of the spill source and any relevant coastal features. It may be useful to draw a grid onto the working copy so that any position can be easily identified by grid reference or, alternatively, by reference to the distance and bearing of a radio beacon. Computer packages that facilitate the planning and recording of flights are also available.

## 3.2 Observing an Oil Spill from an Aircraft

In view of the errors inherent in oil movement forecasting, a systematic aerial search is usually necessary to determine the presence or absence of oil over a large sea area. It will often be carried out as a 'ladder search' (Figures 3.1 & 3.2).

Floating oil has a tendency to become elongated and align parallel to the direction of the wind in long and narrow 'windrows', typically 30 - 50 metres apart. A ladder search across the direction of the prevailing wind increases the chances of oil detection.

Haze and light reflection off the sea often affects visibility of the oil so spotting it is easiest with the

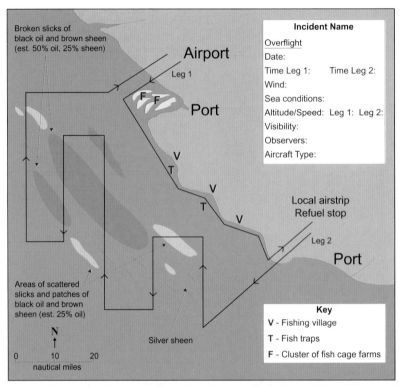

■ **Figure 3.1: An example map showing the flight path and extent of oil observed. In addition to the oil pollution, a range of other features may also be observed during a reconnaissance flight. These might include response and clean-up activities at sea and on shore, the location of sensitive environmental resources such as wildlife and special habitats, together with commercial interests such as amenity areas, industrial sites and mariculture facilities. These may also be annotated on the final plan, or recorded separately, to assist in the strategic response decision-making process. Drawing the flight path on the map shows which areas have been surveyed. The ladder search pattern shown above was adapted to meet expected oil distribution, visibility and light conditions**

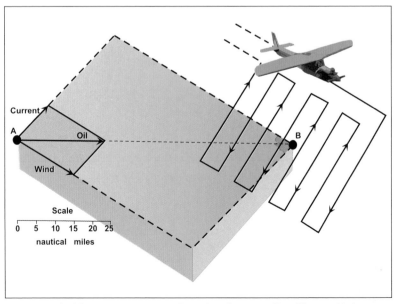

■ **Figure 3.2: Movement of oil from A to position B three days later, predicted by combining 100% of the current speed and 3% of the wind speed as shown. The arrows from A represent current, wind and oil movement for one day. A cross-wind ladder search pattern is shown over position B**

sun behind the observer. Sunglasses with polarising lenses can also assist the detection of oil at sea when light conditions are bright.

Despite careful predictions and a systematic ladder search, the actual pollution observed during the flight may be different to the situation envisaged. It is important, therefore, to adjust for contingency, maximising the chances of plotting the full extent of the spill while still trying to maintain a logical and efficient flight plan.

The search altitude is generally determined by the visibility. Over open sea areas, and in clear weather, 300-450 metres (1000-1500 feet) frequently proves to be optimal for maximising the area scanned without loss of visual clarity.

However, it is necessary to drop to half this height, or lower, to confirm sightings of floating oil or to analyse its appearance. For helicopters, when used closer to shore and in the absence of any restrictions imposed by the pilot or by the nature of the coastline, a flight speed of 150-170 km/h and an altitude of 120-150 metres (400-500 feet) is a useful starting point. Further adjustment may then be made, as appropriate, during the course of the flight.

> Crude and fuel oils spilt at sea undergo marked changes in appearance over time as a result of weathering processes. It is important that observers are familiar with these processes so that the nature of the spill can be accurately reported.

■ Slicks of Iranian light crude oil in warm waters

■ Windrows of black oil and sheen

■ Heavy oil arriving at the shoreline. Benthic seagrass and seabed rock formations can confuse estimations of the amount of oil

■ What appears to be oil is actually freshwater runoff from a narrow creek meeting turbid brackish waters

## Common errors

From the air, it is notoriously difficult to distinguish between oil and a variety of other unrelated phenomena. It is necessary, therefore, to verify initial sightings by overflying the area at an altitude low enough to allow positive identification. Aerial observations of shoreline oiling should be confirmed by a closer inspection from a boat or on foot. Phenomena that most often lead to mistaken reports of oil include:

- Cloud shadows
- ripples on the sea surface
- differences in the colour of two adjacent water masses
- suspended sediments
- floating or suspended organic matter
- floating seaweed
- algal/plankton blooms
- seagrass and coral patches in shallow water
- sewage and industrial discharges.

It is particularly difficult to distinguish between operational tank washings from passing vessels and oil originating from an accidental spill. However, the smaller quantity, coverage and linear distribution of tank washings are usually indicative.

## 3.3 Recording and Reporting Aerial Observations

It is essential that observers can keep track of the position of the aircraft so that progress can be monitored, along with any changes that might be necessary in view of the circumstances noted during the flight. This can be achieved using a portable GPS (Global Positioning System) receiver or GPS fitted within the aircraft.

Features and landmarks along the coast may be compared against charts when surveying a shoreline, but over open water, away from any obvious reference points, it is easy to become disorientated.

Ideally, an observer will have the opportunity of consulting the aircraft instrumentation to ascertain speed, direction and position, so it is worth ensuring beforehand that reading these instruments will present no difficulty.

Observations can be recorded on a laptop or tablet computer with relevant maps downloaded from mapping websites or using electronic shipping charts. A linked GPS receiver can be used to mark

way points for identifying the location of observed oil and other notable features. As a backup to any computer-based system, copies of paper maps and charts, already marked up with pertinent information, can be annotated during the flight.

Throughout the flight communication with fellow observers and the pilot is important for monitoring progress, confirming observations and discussing appropriate adjustments to the flight. Headsets are usually available for this and instruction on their use should be sought before takeoff to avoid disruption with the communications of other aircraft and traffic control authorities.

A report that provides a clear picture of the nature and extent of oil pollution at sea and close to the shore should be compiled promptly after the flight. Records from a succession of flights will also help to provide an understanding of how the situation has developed over time.

The nature of the information collected and the way it needs to be recorded and presented will vary, depending on the scale of the pollution problem.

The main features that should be recorded are provided in Table 3.1.

| Feature | Data | Comment |
|---|---|---|
| **Location and extent** | Latitude and longitude (preferably by GPS) for location of slicks<br><br>GPS readings for centre or edges of large slicks<br><br>Visual estimates for dimensions of smaller slicks and patches | It is important to retain a sense of scale so that what is observed on the water is not exaggerated when recorded. It is worth establishing a mental picture of distance on the outward leg of a flight by observing and noting recognisable land features. When observing large areas affected by oil, the presence of any ships is useful in gauging the scale of slicks. Regular reference to GPS readings is useful to confirm estimates made visually. |
| **Colour** | For oil slicks:<br>Black, brown, orange<br><br>For sheen:<br>Silver, iridescent (rainbow) | Colour offers an important indication of oil thickness. For oil slicks, a brown or orange colour indicates likely presence of water-in-oil emulsion. In terms of oil spill response, sheen may be disregarded as it represents a negligible quantity of oil, cannot be recovered or otherwise dealt with to any significant degree by existing response techniques and is likely to dissipate readily and naturally. Depending on the circumstances, sheen may often be omitted from the final report prepared after the flight. |
| **Character** | Windrow, slick, patch, streak | Observers should avoid too many descriptive phrases and should apply their selected terms consistently throughout. |
| **Features** | Leading edge | If the thick oil characterising the leading edge of a slick can be identified, it should be denoted by a heavier line on the plan and referenced. |
| **Coverage** | <br>25%      50%      75% | For response efforts to be focused on the most significant areas of oil pollution, it is important to have information on the relative and heaviest concentrations. To avoid distorted views it is necessary to look vertically down on the oil when assessing the distribution. It is difficult to make an accurate assessment of the % coverage and it is advisable not to try to be too precise with the estimation. The diagrams may be used as a reference guide. More experienced observers may be able to interpolate intermediate coverages.<br><br>The adoption of common terms can also provide an indication of the amount of oil present in a given area. In combination, the estimate of % coverage, together with selected terms, provides a consistent and flexible method of describing the amount of oil in an area to a degree of accuracy sufficient for response decisions to be made. |
| Traces <10%          Scattered 25%          Patchy 50%          Broken 75%          Continuous >90% | | |

■ **Table 3.1: Main features that should be recorded during a surveillance flight**

■ **Features and landmarks (such as promontories and lighthouses) provide clear reference points when surveying a coastline**

■ **Communication between the aircraft crew and all observers is important to confirm sightings and to discuss changes in the flight plan in the light of observations**

### Sketches
An annotated hand drawn or electronic map should be produced. It is good practice to retain the original sketches and notes in case they need to be referred to again later.

### Photographs
These can also provide a useful record and, whenever possible, features such as ships and the coastline should be included to provide an idea of scale. Digital images can be rapidly disseminated to a wide audience to assist command and control of the response. UV and polarising filters are often useful to cut down glare and sharpen visual definition, although some polarising filters produce colour distortions through aircraft windows made of plastic. A log of the photographs taken should be retained for reference purposes. Dedicated remote sensing aircraft often have built-in downward looking cameras that are linked with a GPS to assign accurate geographic co-ordinates.

### Video
Video is another useful recording tool, but filming may prove difficult in turbulence and during aircraft manoeuvering. The use of hand-held cameras is also constrained by the limited field of view through the eyepiece, which reduces the ability of the observer to quickly scan the sea surface. The presence of an additional observer when video recording is desirable. Downlinks may allow information to be passed automatically to the ground and allow replays. Hand-held video cameras also allow the addition of commentary and, if so, sufficient detail with suitable location references should be given or it may make later coordination with other observations difficult, particularly if extended footage has been produced. Video footage is best used to supplement rather than replace briefings by experienced observers.

## 3.4 Quantifying Floating Oil

An estimate of the quantity of oil observed at sea is important for guidance when planning the required scale of clean-up response. It is crucial, therefore, that during the overflight the observer is able to distinguish between sheen and thicker patches of oil. However, gauging oil thickness and coverage is rarely easy and is made more difficult if the sea is rough. All such estimates should be viewed with caution.

### Thickness
Oils with a low viscosity spread very rapidly, so layers quickly reach an average thickness of about 0.1 mm. However, the thickness of the oil layer can vary considerably within a slick or patch of oil, from less than 0.001 mm to more than 1 mm. The appearance of the oil will provide some indication of its thickness. Emulsions typically contain 50-75% water. Their thickness varies considerably depending on the oil type, the sea conditions and whether the emulsion is free floating or held against a barrier such as a boom or the shoreline. A figure of 1 mm may be used as a guide, but thicknesses of 1 cm and more can sometimes be encountered and it should be emphasised that the thickness of emulsion and other viscous oils is very difficult to gauge because of their limited spreading.

When the sea surface is rough it can also be difficult or impossible to see less buoyant oil types, which can be swamped by waves and remain sub-surface. In cold water some oils with high pour points will solidify into unpredictable shapes and the appearance of the floating portions may disguise the total volume present. The presence of ice floes and snow will confuse the picture further.

■ **Emulsified heavy fuel oil held against the shore by wind and waves. The thickness of the oil is difficult to estimate as the extent to which the oil is pooling in crevasses between the rocks cannot be readily determined from the air**

## Coverage

To estimate the amount of floating oil it is necessary to not only gauge thickness, but also to determine the surface area of the various types of pollution observed. The patchiness of floating oil must be taken into account so that an estimate may be made of the actual area of coverage relative to the total sea area affected. If GPS equipment is not available, the extent of oil must be established by a timed overflight at constant speed.

| Oil Type | Appearance | Approximate Thickness (mm) | Approximate Volume (m³/km²) |
|---|---|---|---|
| Oil sheen | Silver | >0.0001 | 0.1 |
| Oil sheen | Iridescent | >0.0003 | 0.3 |
| Crude and fuel oil | Brown to black | >0.1 | 100 |
| Water-in-oil emulsion | Brown/orange | >1 | >1000 |

■ **Table 3.2:** A guide to the relationship between appearance, thickness and volume of floating oil

 It is possible to estimate the order of magnitude of a spill, but any estimate should be viewed with considerable caution because of the uncertainties involved.

The following example provides an illustration of the process of estimating oil quantities:

During aerial reconnaissance flown at a constant speed of 250 km/hr, crude oil emulsion and silver sheen were observed floating within a sea area, the length and width of which required 65 seconds and 35 seconds to overfly. The percentage cover of emulsion patches was estimated at 10% and the percentage cover of sheen at 90%. From this information it was calculated that the length of the contaminated area of sea was:

$$\frac{65\,(\text{seconds}) \times 250\,(\text{km/hr})}{3600\,(\text{seconds in one hour})} = 4.5\ \text{km}$$

The width of the sea area measured was:

$$\frac{35 \times 250}{3600} = 2.4\ \text{km}$$

This provided a total area of approximately 11 square kilometres or 3.2 square nautical miles.

Using the approximate volume in m³ per km² (Table 3.2), the volume of emulsion for the example given could be calculated as 10% (coverage) of 11 (km²) × 1000. As 50-75% of this emulsion is likely to be water, the volume of oil present would amount to approximately 275-550 m³.

A similar calculation for the volume of sheen yields 90% of 11 × 0.1, equivalent to approximately 1 m³ of oil.

This example also demonstrates that although sheen may cover a relatively large area of sea surface, it often makes only a negligible contribution to the volume of oil present.

## 3.5 Remote Sensing

Visual observation and photography are the most common forms of oil spill monitoring, but they can be supplemented by airborne remote sensing equipment that detects radiation outside the visible spectrum and provides additional information about the oil. Remote sensing is increasingly used to monitor, detect and identify sources of illegal marine discharges, but can also be used to monitor accidental oil spills.

Remote sensors work by detecting different properties of the sea surface, which are modified by the presence of oil.

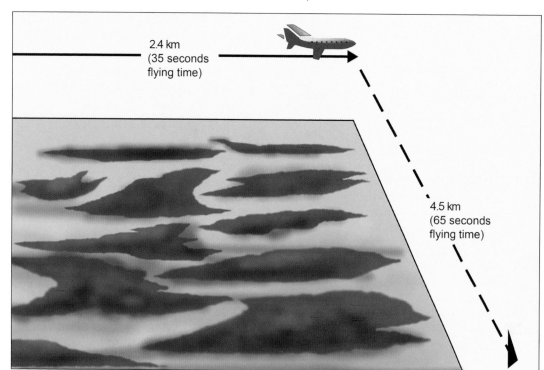

2.4 km
(35 seconds flying time)

4.5 km
(65 seconds flying time)

■ **Figure 3.3: Aerial calculations of volume**

- Colour

- reflectance

- temperature or roughness.

The most commonly employed combinations of sensors include:

- Side looking airborne radar (SLAR)

- downward looking thermal infrared (IR)

- ultraviolet (UV) detectors or imaging systems.

Additional information can be obtained using systems, such as:

- Forward looking infrared (FLIR)

- microwave radiometers (MWR)

- laser fluorosensors (LF)

- compact airborne spectrographic imagers (CASI).

All sensors require trained personnel to operate them and to interpret the results.

The majority of remote sensing systems are bulky and can only be used from the dedicated aircraft into which they are installed. However, hand-held IR cameras are available and provide a portable remote sensing system that is not limited to dedicated aircraft.

UV, thermal IR, FLIR, MWR, and CASI are all passive sensors, measuring emitted or reflected radiation. With the possible exception of MWR, they cannot penetrate cloud cover, fog, haze or rain so their use is limited to clear weather periods.

SLAR and LF incorporate an active source of radiation and rely on sophisticated electronic analysis of the return signal to detect oil and, in the case of LF, provide some indication of the type of oil. MWR can provide information on the thickness of oil on the sea surface but are unable to do so if the oil has emulsified. Sensors relying on MWR and LF imaging systems can normally only provide information on oil along a narrow track immediately beneath the aircraft. MWR, LF and IR sensors can all be used at night in clear skies, while radar systems can also penetrate cloud or fog, day and night and are, therefore, able to operate under most conditions, although they are less effective in both calm weather and strong winds.

A combination of different devices is often used to overcome the limitations of individual sensors and to provide better information about the extent and nature of the oil. Combined SLAR and IR/UV systems have been used fairly widely during oil spills. SLAR can be flown at a high enough altitude to provide a rapid sweep over a wide area, up to 20 nautical miles either side of the aircraft. However, SLAR is unable to distinguish between very thin layers of sheen and thicker oil patches, so the images must be interpreted with caution. Aircraft equipped with a combination of SLAR and IR can define the total extent of the slick (using SLAR) and then, once the oil has been located, provide qualitative information on slick thickness and the areas of heavier pollution with images from the IR sensors. In daylight an IR/UV sensor combination can fulfil a similar function. The UV sensor detects all of the oil covered area, irrespective of thickness, while the thermal IR sensor is capable, under appropriate conditions, of delineating the relatively thick layers.

Signals from all types of sensor are usually displayed and recorded on equipment onboard the aircraft. If they are to be used effectively for the management of the response operations, images must be relayed to the command centre quickly, correctly interpreted and then presented in a concise and understandable format. In order that the results from remote sensing systems are correctly interpreted,

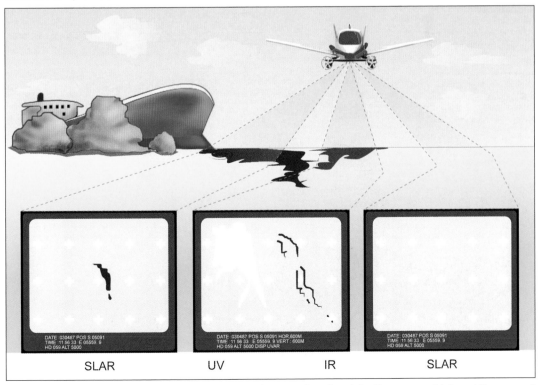

■ **Remote sensing aircraft fitted with side looking airborne radar, ultraviolet line scan and infrared line scan oil detection systems**

it is usually advisable to confirm the findings with visual observations.

## Satellite imagery

Satellite-based remote sensors can also detect oil on water and, because these images cover extensive sea areas, they can provide a comprehensive picture of the overall extent of pollution. The sensors used include those operating in the visible and infrared regions of the spectrum and synthetic aperture radar (SAR). SAR is not limited by the presence of cloud and, as it does not rely on reflected light, also remains operational at night. However, radar imagery often includes a number of anomalous features that can be mistaken for oil, such as wind shadows and rain squalls, and so requires expert interpretation. A further limitation of all satellite imagery is that the frequency with which a satellite passes over the same areas ranges from a few days to weeks, depending on the particular orbit. This delay can be partially overcome by interrogation of more than one satellite platform and, where possible, by positioning the satellite's transmitter beam at different angles on a given path. In addition, the systems onboard usually have to be instructed to acquire the imagery from the area of interest. The imagery then has to be transmitted from a ground receiving station for interpretation. Processing time has previously limited the use of satellite imagery in oil spill response, but for some systems this has now decreased sufficiently for it to be a useful operational tool. Satellite images can also be used at a later stage to complement aerial observations and provide a wider picture of the extent of pollution.

### EVOIKOS – Straits of Singapore, 1997

Following a collision in the Singapore Straits on 15 October 1997, the EVOIKOS suffered damage to three cargo tanks, spilling approximately 29,000 tonnes of heavy fuel oil. The spilt oil initially affected the waters and some southern islands of Singapore, but later oil slicks drifted in the Malaysian and Indonesian waters of the Malacca Straits. After over two months afloat, oil came ashore along a 40 km stretch of the Malaysian coast in December 1997.

The Maritime and Port Authority in Singapore had an agreement with the Centre for Remote Imaging, Sensing and Processing (CRISP) of the National University of Singapore for the provision of satellite data to track the spread of oil spills. Oil slicks are identifiable in SAR imagery as dark patches, which can be discriminated easily from the sea. This is due to differences in surface roughness of open waters and oil-covered areas. Other phenomena, such as wind and rain, can also create dark patches, so expert analysis was required to distinguish oil from other features.

Due to previous sensor commitments and regional atmospheric pollution, it was not possible to obtain an image of the spill in its early stages, but satellite imagery was used subsequently to monitor the threat as the slick spread over more than 3,000 km² of sea surface. The SAR images, received from the Canadian remote sensing satellite, RADARSAT-1, were processed using filtering and fuzzy classification techniques to enhance the detection of oil.

Analysis of the images from this incident clearly identified distinct regions of high, medium and low concentrations of oil, allowing the extent of the spill to be mapped and preparations made for a coordinated response.

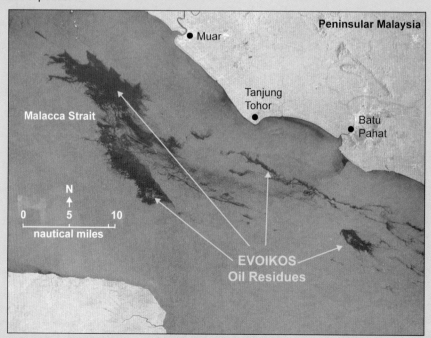

■ A sythetic aperture radar satellite image of the southern Malacca Strait taken after the EVOIKOS spill in Singapore, showing the oil residues while they were moving north-west with the current.
Image kindly provided by RADARSAT International © Canadian Space Agency 1997. Received and processed by CRISP, National University of Singapore and distributed under licence by RADARSAT International

■ **Oil on a cobble shore**

The arrival of oil on shore may be the first indication of an oil pollution incident. Depending on the quantity and type of oil involved, a clean-up response may have to be organised to remove it and protect sensitive areas nearby. A reliable early report and estimate of the extent of the pollution can prove invaluable for organising the most appropriate clean-up equipment and manpower for the task. Estimating the amount of stranded oil with accuracy is difficult, and even identifying the type of oil can be a problem, particularly if the oil has weathered extensively. For large spills the source of stranded oil may be obvious, but the question of identification frequently arises when a small amount of oil is involved.

## 4.1 Types and Sources of Oil Pollution

■ **A pipeline can become a source of chronic leakage or suffer an abrupt rupture**

### Crude oil
This will usually originate from oil rigs, pipelines and tankers, and it is typically a black liquid when fresh. As the lighter components evaporate the viscosity will increase and the oil may start to incorporate water to form an emulsion, which is usually brown, red or orange in colour. Stranded emulsions often release water under a hot sun, reverting to the appearance of black oil. Eventually, the residue of stranded oil assumes a non-sticky consistency, similar to tar.

### Fuel oil
This is carried by ships as either cargo or bunker fuel. It can be difficult to distinguish between heavy fuel oil and weathered crude oil on the shoreline, particularly as fuel oil may also form stable emulsions. Following an incident involving a tanker, both types of oil may be washed ashore, either separately or as a mixture.

### Refined petroleum products
These are relatively light and volatile products and they are unlikely to persist when spilt because of their rapid spreading and high evaporation rates. Lubricating oils are relatively non-volatile and therefore an exception, but they can be identified by their resemblance to car engine oil and a tendency to form discrete lenses or saucer shapes when deposited on sand.

■ **A translucent base oil, used in the manufacture of lubricating oils, has formed lenses on the water's surface**

### Vegetable oils
These include products such as palm oil, rapeseed oil and olive oil. In general, vegetable oils behave in a similar way to petroleum oils in the initial stages of a spill and tend to float and spread on the surface of the water. They are, however, less soluble in water than petroleum oils and do not disperse or evaporate to any extent. Vegetable oils do not readily form water-in-oil emulsions, but may undergo a process of polymerisation to form rubbery strings and clumps. Several oils in this category are characterised by rancid smells distinct from petroleum. They may be translucent, white or vivid yellow/red in appearance, depending on the degree of processing and other factors.

■ **A spill of palm oil**

### Waste oils, greases and slops

Waste oils and greases, generated as part of routine ship operations, and slops, typically comprising tank washing residues, accumulate in ship bilges and slop tanks. If the correct oil/water separation and monitoring procedures are not followed, or if associated equipment has malfunctioned, discharges of oily bilge water or slops from any vessel can lead to pollution. The resulting oil mixture often arrives ashore in the form of viscous patches, tarry lumps or tarballs.

A substantial volume of oil reaches the sea through urban runoff into rivers, through discharges from land-based industries and through effluents from municipal sewers. However, the concentration of oil in these discharges is seldom high enough to cause gross contamination of the shoreline, although sometimes brown bands or oily sheen may be seen in the tide marks left by waves on a sandy beach.

## 4.2 Appearance and Persistence of Oil on Shorelines

■ **Fresh fuel oil on a rocky shore**

The appearance and persistence of stranded oil depends to a large extent on the type of coastline, which can vary from exposed rocky shores through pebble and sand beaches to sheltered muddy marshes. Oil pollution is seldom uniform in either thickness or coverage. Contamination can range from pools of liquid oil to light staining or sheen. Winds, waves and currents cause oil to be deposited ashore in streaks or patches, rather than as a continuous layer. On tidal shores the zone affected can be comparatively wide, particularly on flat, sheltered beaches, but elsewhere the pollution is often confined to a narrow band close to the high water mark.

Oil that initially coats a sandy beach can soon be partly covered with sand by wind and wave action. Digging may reveal one or several layers of oil that have become buried by clean sand.

Liquid oils with a low viscosity will soak into sand to some extent, depending on the composition, grain size and moisture content of the substrate. For example, wet quartz sand composed of small grains will absorb less oil than coarse dry shell sand. Penetration into larger beach substrate such as pebble and shingle can reach substantial depths.

 The rate of weathering processes such as evaporation, oxidation and biodegradation determines the persistence of stranded oil.

The most active processes of oil removal from shorelines are usually abrasion and physical dispersion, accelerated by elevated temperatures and exposure to wave action. Tarballs, which are otherwise very resistant to weathering, may soften in strong sunlight and become more amenable to degradation. However, thin layers of oil exposed to strong sunlight can become baked onto solid surfaces such as rock, and be difficult to remove. Nevertheless, wave action can eventually reduce even the most persistent lumps of oil to smaller fragments that are then more readily attacked by chemical and biological processes. On sheltered shores, where there is less wave energy, the oil may persist for longer periods. If oil becomes buried in soft sediment it is protected from wave action and degradation may be inhibited by the lack of oxygen. Significant breakdown will only resume if the buried oil is exposed again by erosion, tilling or other actions.

■ **Streaks of oil on a sandy beach**

■ **Oil and oily substrate buried between layers of clean sand by wave action**

A number of naturally occurring features can be confused with oil and a close examination of reported pollution is advisable.

Silvery or multi-coloured sheens of biological origin covering the surface of rock pools give the appearance of oil, but are often the result of biological processes, e.g. bacterial degradation. Similar effects are associated with peat outcrops in marshy areas.

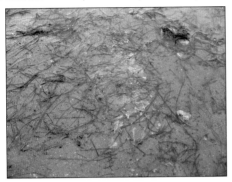

■ **Natural sheen produced by rotting seagrass**

Algae or lichen on rocks, stranded seaweed, black mineral sand, charred wood particles, coal, volcanic sand, pumice and wet sediment or roots can all resemble oil from a distance.

■ **Coal dust resembling oil on a sandy beach**

On some beaches, it is possible to dig down to an oxygen-free layer, often grey or black in colour and smelling of rotting vegetation. This is a normal feature and should not be mistaken for oil.

■ **Digging exposes black anoxic sediment**

## 4.3 Describing and Quantifying Stranded Oil

A rough assessment of the quantity of oil present on a stretch of coastline is essential for planning an appropriate response and for monitoring its progress. It is also useful to understand where spilt oil naturally accumulates; for example, in small coves and inlets and under jetties, piers and other manmade structures. From these locations trapped oil can readily remobilise and contaminate other areas.

The variable distribution of oil on shorelines makes the task of estimating the quantity of stranded oil difficult, so it should be approached with care and consistency. The assessment is largely a visual one and it will be impossible if the oil is hidden from view, by beach substrate, snow or mangroves for example.

Where the oil is visible the task can be addressed in two stages.

### Stage One - Extent of contamination
The overall extent of the contamination along a coastline can be estimated and marked on a chart or map. Aerial observation is usually the most efficient and convenient way of gaining a general impression, and this should be combined with spot checks on foot, or 'ground truthing', for a more accurate assessment. Careful attention should be given to the identification of locations where the character of the shoreline changes or where the degree of oil coverage appears to change.

Reports of shore pollution should include the location, date and time of the observations, the parts of the shore affected and the extent, the type of substrate and key shoreline features. Reports should also record a description of the oil itself. Considering the possible sources of the spill and noting the oil's consistency and smell will often give clues to its identity.

The use of GPS and photographs is a useful support to any written description of the location and appearance of oil on shorelines. Photographs also serve as a record against which later changes in the degree of pollution may be compared. When oiled sites are to be visited on more than one occasion, it is useful to take photographs from specific reference points so that they may be easily compared.

### Stage Two - Amount of oil
Representative samples of shoreline should be selected to calculate the amount of oil present. It is useful to split the shoreline into segments based on the shoreline type and the degree of contamination. The sample area chosen should be small enough to allow a reliable estimation of oil volume in a reasonable time, yet large enough to be representative of the whole shore section similarly affected. The dimensions of the section of beach affected by oil should be estimated and, if the degree of contamination is consistent, the average thickness of oil should be relatively easy to measure. If the degree of oiling varies from the low to high tide lines, a representative strip of the beach, for example one metre wide running from the top of the beach to the water's edge, should be surveyed. The oil thickness in a representative number of locations within the strip should be estimated and

multiplied by the area of the strip. This figure can then be multiplied by the length of the entire beach to estimate the total volume of oil. The exercise has to be repeated on other sections as the nature of the shoreline or the degree of oil coverage may be different.

Quantifying stranded oil in this way yields only an approximate figure because of several unavoidable sources of error. On a sandy beach the affected area can be calculated relatively easily, but the possibility of oil penetrating into the beach substrate should be remembered. Oil penetration is likely to be greater as the grain size of the beach substrate increases and so the larger the grain size, the more difficult it can be to estimate the volume of oil on the shoreline. Occasionally, the volume of oil that has penetrated will be impossible to estimate but, when sand is uniformly saturated, a useful rule of thumb is that the pure oil content is approximately one tenth of the depth of oily sand. For example, if oil has penetrated uniformly to a depth of 5 cm, the volume of oil below the surface would be approximately $0.005 \ m^3/m^2$ or 5 litres/m². Furthermore, when calculating oil volumes the occurrence of water-in-oil emulsions can be misleading. Stable emulsions typically contain 40 – 80% water, i.e. the volume of 'pure' oil may be as little as 20% of the observed volume of pollutant. The presence of debris or stones and crevices on rocky shores can be an added complication.

■ **Oil stranding on a coastline covered in debris is difficult to quantify**

💧 **If in some situations it is impractical to use the relatively time consuming methods outlined, it should be possible to estimate the percentage coverage and/or describe the degree of pollution as 'light', 'moderate' or 'heavy'.**

Often, the most compelling reason for quantifying stranded oil is to facilitate clean-up. Therefore, the total amount of oily material, as opposed to the amount of oil spilt, is the most relevant figure as any debris, sand or water mixed with the oil will also require removal. However, on sandy beaches it is worth noting that removal of oil-saturated sand may involve a quantity of material at least ten times greater than the oil itself. This may lead to problems with beach erosion, temporary storage and final disposal of the collected material.

Quantification of shoreline oiling has been formalised in some countries in a process known as SCAT (shoreline clean-up assessment team or

technique). During a SCAT survey, trained personnel methodically record geo-referenced observations on prepared forms (see page 36) using specific and standard terminology. Such descriptions and definitions allow a comparison over time and between different sites, allowing observers to build a spatial image of the nature and extent of shoreline oiling.

Unpolluted sandy beach.

Light oil pollution – Less than 10 ml oil/m².

Moderate oil pollution – 10 ml-1 litre oil/m².

Heavy oil pollution – 1-100 litres oil/m².

■ **The degree of pollution may be described as 'light', 'moderate' or 'heavy' against standard references**

The information gathered from the quantification and description of the oil can be used during various stages of the response, including decision-making and planning of response operations, monitoring, termination and subsequent damage assessment. An understanding of the full nature and extent of shoreline oiling is key to the comparison and prioritisation of oiled sites and helps when planning resources, manpower and the time required for shoreline clean-up. Knowledge of the quantity of oily material is also important when determining waste storage, transportation and disposal needs.

## 4.4  Sampling Guidelines

Oil pollution that causes damage or necessitates shoreline clean-up may lead to claims for compensation. Evidence linking the damage or costs incurred to the alleged polluter will be required. Sometimes the link is easy to demonstrate, for example, when the source is obvious and the oil has not travelled far, but on occasions it is necessary to analyse oil samples taken from the suspected source(s) and the polluted site. In cases where the source of a spill of bunker fuel is in question, sophisticated 'fingerprinting' of samples may be necessary to identify distinguishing characteristics between similar samples.

> Where there is doubt about the source of contamination or the possibility of claims for compensation, samples of the oil from suspect sources ('reference samples') should be taken cooperatively. Each sample can be split between the interested parties to allow for independent analysis as necessary.

On occasion, a more extensive sampling plan may be warranted. For example, it can be helpful to monitor the concentration of hydrocarbons in the water column to demonstrate a return to background levels in order to guide decision-making, particularly with regard to fisheries restrictions. Agreement on the reason for sampling and the criteria for decision-making should be reached prior to beginning the sampling. This approach will also help to determine the scope and duration of the monitoring programme. A sampling plan need not be complex or extensive, but should include:

- The number of sampling stations and their location (e.g. GPS position), including reference or control sites

- a description of the samples to be taken (e.g. surface oil, water, sediment, biota etc) and the quantity

- instruction for possible replicate and duplicate samples

- the frequency of sampling

- sampling procedures to be followed (e.g. surface skimming, sediment grabs, subsurface sampling etc)

- protocols for handling, preserving, storage and transport of samples (e.g. containers to be used, labelling, stabilisation, chain of custody and customs documentation etc)

- analysis protocols to be followed.

■ **Sampling stranded oil on the shoreline**

Reference may be made to the International Maritime Organization's guidelines for sampling and identification of oils, which provide guidance on the techniques, equipment and strategies for sampling oil, with particular emphasis on the field work required to collect samples.

## SHORELINE OILING SUMMARY (SOS) FORM — for _____ Spill    Page _____ of _____

**1  GENERAL INFORMATION** | Date (dd/mm/yy) | Time (24h): standard/daylight | Tide Height

Segment ID:

Operations Division:

hrs to _____ hrs    rising / falling

Survey by:  Foot / ATV / Boat / Helicopter / Overlook / _____    Sun / Clouds / Fog / Rain / Snow / Windy / Calm

**2  SURVEY TEAM #** _____    name         organization              contact phone number

| | | |
|---|---|---|
| | | |
| | | |
| | | |
| | | |
| | | |

**3  SEGMENT**    Total Segment Length _____ m    Segment Length Surveyed _____ m

**Start GPS:**  LATITUDE _____ deg.  _____ min.  LONGITUDE _____ deg.  _____ min.

**End GPS:**  LATITUDE _____ deg.  _____ min.  LONGITUDE _____ deg.  _____ min.

**Differential GPS**  Yes / No

**4A  SHORELINE TYPE**        select only one primary (P) oiled shoreline type and any secondary (S)

| BEDROCK : ____ | MANMADE SOLID : ____ | SEDIMENT BEACH : | Sand ____ | SEDIMENT FLATS : | Mud Flats ____ |
|---|---|---|---|---|---|
| cliff/vertical ____  sloping ____  platform ____ | | Pebble-Cobble ____ | Boulder ____ | Sand Flats ____ | Sand-Gravel ____ |
| Winter Only: Ice Foot ____   Snow ____ | | Mixed Sand-Gravel ____ | MARSH : ____ | Peb-Cob ____ | Boulder ____ |

**4B  COASTAL CHARACTER**        backshore character — select only one primary (P) and any secondary (S)

CLIFF or HILL : _____ : est. height _____ m    Beach ____    Delta ___    Tidal inlet ___    Marsh/Wetland ___

slope: gentle (<5 deg.) ___ medium ___ steep (>30 deg.)    Barrier beach ____    Dune ___    Channel ___    other _____

**5  OPERATIONAL FEATURES** _____    debris Y / N    oiled? Y / N    debris amount: _____ bags OR _____ trucks

direct backshore access            Y / N    suitable backshore staging  Y / N

alongshore access from next segment  Y / N    access restrictions _____

**6  SURFACE OILING CONDITIONS**        begin with 'A' in the lowest tidal zone

| OIL ZONE ID | TIDAL ZONE | | | | OIL COVER | | | OIL THICKNESS | | | | | OIL CHARACTER | | | | | | | SUBST. TYPE(S) |
|---|---|---|---|---|---|---|---|---|---|---|---|---|---|---|---|---|---|---|---|---|
| | LI | MI | UI | SU | Length m | Width m | Distrib. % | PO | CV | CT | ST | FL | FR | MS | TB | PT | TC | SR | AP | NO | |
| A | | | | | | | | | | | | | | | | | | | | | |
| | | | | | | | | | | | | | | | | | | | | | |
| | | | | | | | | | | | | | | | | | | | | | |
| | | | | | | | | | | | | | | | | | | | | | |
| | | | | | | | | | | | | | | | | | | | | | |
| | | | | | | | | | | | | | | | | | | | | | |

**7  SUBSURFACE OILING CONDITIONS**        use letter for ZONE location plus Number of pit or trench — e.g., 'A1'

| TRENCH or PIT NO. | TIDAL ZONE | | | | MAX. PIT DEPTH cm | OILED ZONE cm-cm | SUBSURFACE OIL CHARACTER | | | | | | | WATER TABLE cm | SHEEN COLOUR B, R, S, N | CLEAN BELOW Yes / No | SUBST. TYPE(S) |
|---|---|---|---|---|---|---|---|---|---|---|---|---|---|---|---|---|---|
| | LI | MI | UI | SU | | | SAP | OP | PP | OR | OF | TR | NO | | | | |
| | | | | | | | | | | | | | | | | | |
| | | | | | | | | | | | | | | | | | |
| | | | | | | | | | | | | | | | | | |
| | | | | | | | | | | | | | | | | | |
| | | | | | | | | | | | | | | | | | |
| | | | | | | | | | | | | | | | | | |

**8  COMMENTS**    (clean-up recommendations — ecological/recreational/cultural/economic issues & constraints — wildlife obs.)

Sketch Yes/No    Photos Yes/No (Roll # _____ Frames _____ )    Video Tape Yes/No (tape # _____ )    ver. 05/01

**Figure 4.1: A SCAT survey shoreline oiling form. This is the standard form relating to temperate tidal environments (source: Environment Canada)**

# ENVIRONMENTAL EFFECTS OF OIL SPILLS 5

Oil spills in the marine environment can have serious effects on wildlife, fisheries and coastal and marine habitats. However, while damage occurs and may be profound at the level of individual organisms, as a general rule the effects of oil spills are short lived and localised. The ability of animal and plant populations to recover from an oil spill, and the time taken for a normal functioning habitat to be re-established, depends on the severity and duration of the disturbance and the recovery potential of the individual species.

The impact of oil on marine life is caused by either its physical nature (physical contamination and smothering) or by its chemical components (toxic effects and accumulation leading to tainting). The animals and plants most vulnerable are those that could come into contact with a contaminated sea surface, such as seabirds that feed by diving, some marine mammals and reptiles, marine life on shorelines and animals and plants in mariculture facilities. The extent to which organisms are sensitive to oil pollution is also important as less sensitive organisms are more likely to withstand short-term exposure.

**Vulnerable resources** are those that are most likely to come into contact with oil because of their positioning in the marine environment, typically at the sea surface or on the water's edge. Examples include diving birds and intertidal species such as limpets.

**Sensitive resources** are those that would be acutely affected by exposure to oil or its component chemicals. Examples include mangroves and fish larvae.

 Marine life forms may also be affected by clean-up operations, or indirectly through physical damage to the habitats in which they live.

■ **Oil spills can have marked, but usually short-term, effects on shoreline communities**

The exact nature and duration of any effects from a spill depend on a number of factors, including:

- The type and amount of oil and its behaviour once spilt
- the physical characteristics of the affected area

- weather conditions and season
- the type and effectiveness of the clean-up response
- the biological and economic characteristics of the area and their sensitivity to oil pollution.

**Physical contamination**

Oil that is highly persistent, floats and is spilt in a large quantity, such as a cargo of heavy fuel oil, has the potential to cause widespread damage at the sea surface by preventing marine life from carrying out normal functions, such as feeding, respiration and movement. In contrast, lighter oils and products are less persistent, tend to evaporate quickly in most circumstances and, therefore, have less opportunity to cause physical damage to sensitive organisms.

■ **Seabirds that feed by diving are vulnerable to oil spills**

Effects can be expected to be greatest in situations where dilution is slowed, such as when oil becomes trapped in sediment or within enclosed areas like shallow lagoons with poor water exchange.

**Chemical contamination**

Marine organisms can take up low concentrations of oil components in the surrounding seawater and retain them to varying degrees. Sedentary animals in shallow waters, such as oysters, mussels and clams that routinely filter large volumes of seawater to extract food, are particularly susceptible. Damage through toxicity is most likely with light oils.

The presence of toxic components does not always cause mortality, but may induce temporary effects such as narcosis and tainting of tissues, which usually subside over time.

## 5.1 Environmental Impacts

The ability of plants and animals to survive contamination by oil varies. This is due not only to inherent differences between species, but also to the influence of other factors. For example, populations living at the extreme of their geographical range may be particularly at risk. In addition, the different life stages of a species may show widely different tolerances and reactions to oil pollution. Usually the eggs, larval and juvenile stages will be more susceptible than adult stages.

When considering the environmental impacts of oil spills, it is important to recognise that the marine ecosystem is highly complex and that natural fluctuations in species composition, abundance and distribution are normal. Against this background of variability, subtle effects due to an oil spill may be difficult to detect. Furthermore, spills are not the only stressor on marine habitats; chronic urban and industrial contamination, or the exploitation of the resources they provide, are also serious threats.

The key to determining the significance of any damage is whether the oil has caused a depression in breeding success, productivity, diversity and the normal functioning of the system. From an ecological point of view, it is the health of the populations of animals and plants and the integrity of their habitats that is more important than the status of individuals.

### 5.1.1 Impact of Oil on Specific Marine Organisms and Habitats

**Plankton**
Plankton is the generic term describing floating plants and animals carried passively by water currents in the upper layers of the sea. They play a crucial role in the marine food chain. Because populations are patchy and variable over time, plankton is extremely difficult to study reliably. Toxic and sub-lethal effects on plankton caused by oil have been demonstrated in the laboratory and there is little doubt that there is potential for impact. However, plankton is abundant and is replenished by the constant movement of the water body and there is no evidence to suggest that oil spills have caused a significant decline in populations in the open sea.

**Fish**
Fish kills in open water following an oil spill are rare, as most adult free swimming fish will move away from oil contaminated water. In addition, the likelihood that oil concentrations at sea will be high enough to affect fish populations is very small. Spilt oil poses a much greater threat in shallow or enclosed waters or to fish eggs and larvae that cannot actively avoid or escape a pollution event. As well as mortality, oil may cause more subtle longer term damage to behaviour, feeding, growth or reproductive functions.

**Seabirds**
Seabirds are among the most vulnerable inhabitants of open waters and they are easily harmed by floating oil. Species that dive for their food or that congregate on the sea surface are particularly at risk. Although oil ingested by birds during attempts to clean themselves by preening may be lethal, the most common causes of death are drowning, starvation and loss of body heat following fouling of plumage by oil. Oil contamination of eggs can lead to eggshell thinning, the failure of the egg to hatch and developmental abnormalities.

Cleaning and rehabilitation after oiling is often attempted, but for many species it is rare for more than a fraction of oiled birds to survive cleaning and rarer still for those that survive to breed

successfully after release. Penguins are an exception and are much more resilient than most other birds. When handled properly, the majority are likely to survive the cleaning process and rejoin breeding populations.

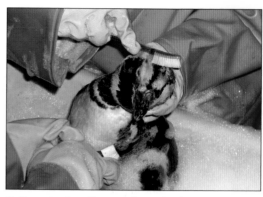

■ **Penguins benefit more than other bird species from cleaning and often fully recover**

Bird mortality occurs during most spills and in some major spills breeding colonies have been seriously depleted. Some species react to colony depletion by laying more eggs, breeding more frequently or having younger birds join the breeding group. These processes can assist the recovery of the colony, although it may take several years and will also depend on other factors, such as food supply.

---

**SEA EMPRESS – Wales, UK, 1996**

On 15 February 1996, the tanker SEA EMPRESS, ran aground at the entrance of the port of Milford Haven, Wales, spilling some 72,000 tonnes of Forties Blend North Sea crude oil and 370 tonnes of heavy fuel oil.

One of the conspicuous acute impacts following the spill was heavy bird mortality. In total, 7,000 oiled birds were washed ashore and it is almost certain that many more birds will have been killed and washed out to sea. The worst hit species was a black sea duck, the common scoter (*melanitta nigra*). Scoters spend much time on the surface of the water and dive to the seabed for food, typically bivalves and other invertebrates such as polychaetes and amphipods, which leaves them particularly susceptible to oiling. Some 4,600 oiled scoters were collected, of which 3,500 were dead or died in cleaning centres; this represents about 5% of the UK wintering population. The following season, numbers of common scoter visiting Carmarthen Bay were well below normal, at 10,000 fewer than the peak in 1995/6. In addition to direct mortality, the loss and contamination of their food resources and disturbances from the clean-up operation are likely to have contributed to this downturn. The change may also, in part, be due to natural variability, as numbers normally fluctuate from year to year. The population of common scoters in Carmarthen Bay had recovered to pre-spill levels in the third winter after the spill, and remained relatively consistent ten years after the incident. The effects of the SEA EMPRESS on local common scoter numbers and distribution, and by implication the ecosystem that supports them, appear to have been short-lived.

While it is common for short and medium term loss to occur in bird populations, there is scant evidence of spills causing long-term harm to populations, or of a spill tipping a marginal colony into permanent decline.

## Sea mammals and reptiles

Whales and dolphins are highly mobile and do not appear to be particularly at risk from oil spills. Dugongs and manatees may be more vulnerable because they typically live in shallow, protected areas, such as bays and mangrove channels, where oil may become trapped. Coastal mammals such as seals and otters that spend time on the shoreline are also more likely to encounter oil. Species that rely on fur to regulate their body temperature are the most sensitive to oil since, if the fur becomes matted with oil, the animals may die from hypothermia or overheating, depending on the season.

■ Oil can become matted in the fur of a seal pup and damage its insulation

Marine reptiles, such as turtles, are also vulnerable to oil, particularly through contamination of their nesting sites, which are typically located on sandy beaches. Adults can suffer inflammation of their mucus membrane, increasing susceptibility to infection. However, there are many cases where oiled turtles have been successfully cleaned and returned to the sea.

## Coastal Waters

In shallow waters, damaging environmental effects are most often caused by oil becoming mixed into the sea by wave action. In many circumstances the dilution capacity is sufficient to keep concentrations in the water below harmful levels, but in major incidents where heavy wave action has dispersed large volumes of oil close inshore, large kills of marine organisms such as shellfish have occurred.

On a few occasions, for example the BRAER spill in Shetland, UK, spilt oil dispersed naturally at sea through heavy wave action, thus avoiding much of the shoreline contamination normally associated with large oil spills. However, this led to the incorporation of oil into seabed sediments and caused long-term contamination of certain benthic commercial species.

It is unlikely that any clean-up technique will damage life in the open sea, but restrictions on the use of dispersants are often imposed near spawning grounds or in some sheltered, nearshore waters where dilution capacity is poor. The deliberate sinking of floating oil is not advisable as this may smother organisms living at the bottom of the sea.

## Shorelines

Under the influence of winds and currents, nearshore spills will inevitably lead to shoreline oiling, the extent of which will depend on the severity of the circumstances.

- **Rocky and sandy shores**

  Rocky and sandy shores exposed to wave action and the scouring effects of tidal currents tend to be most resilient to the effects of a spill as they usually naturally clean quite rapidly. While intertidal animals and plants are resistant to short-term adverse conditions they may, however, be killed by toxic oil components or smothered by viscous and weathered oils and emulsions. Animals may also become narcotised by the oil and, as a consequence, become detached from rock surfaces or emerge from burrows. They are then susceptible to predators or

### EXXON VALDEZ – Alaska, USA, 1989

The EXXON VALDEZ grounded on Bligh Reef in Prince William Sound, Alaska, on 24 March 1989, spilling about 37,000 tonnes of Alaska North Slope crude. The oil spread widely, affecting a variety of shores to varying degrees over an estimated 1,800 km in Prince William Sound and along Alaska's south coast.

The EXXON VALDEZ is the most studied oil spill in terms of long-term impacts, but scientists dispute the magnitude of the damage and the duration of effects. Sea otters are one of a number of species that have been intensely scrutinised by researchers.

The short-term effects of the spill on sea otters inhabiting the coastal waters of Prince William Sound were obvious and acute. By September 1989 almost 1,000 dead otters had been found in the spill area and estimates of total mortality in the aftermath of the incident ranged as high as 2,650. A number of studies indicated that sea otter populations also exhibited prolonged effects after the spill. In some regions of Prince William Sound, research indicated that sea otter abundance had not recovered over ten years later, although some areas recorded otter numbers as equivalent to or higher than pre-spill levels. Other studies found that the mortality of recently weaned juveniles in the winters of 1990/91 and 1992/3 was higher in oiled areas than uncontaminated sites and that the mortality of prime-age sea otters was also higher than normal after the spill. Continued exposure to oil trapped in intertidal sediments through foraging and contamination via their prey may have contributed to persistent spill effects. However, some of the measured variations in sea otter populations may have resulted from local movements of otters or area-wide population effects. Because of the lack of reliable data on the density and distribution of animal populations before the incident, an assessment of long-term population effects of the EXXON VALDEZ oil spill to sea otters remains inconclusive.

to being washed into an area where they cannot survive. A typical example of impact on this habitat is the temporary loss of grazing species, such as limpets, leading to a rapid growth or 'green flush' of seaweeds in their absence, which then dominate the shore in the short-term. Because of the increased availability of their food source, re-colonisation by limpets usually follows and the normal grazing pattern is re-established, typically within one to three years.

■ **Although limpets may survive the presence of residual oil due to their protective shell, they are susceptible to the toxic and smothering effects of gross contamination**

In some circumstances, subtle changes to rocky shore communities can be triggered by a spill or the clean-up, which can be detected for ten or more years. Although the functioning, diversity and productivity of the ecosystem is restored, the distribution of a particular species may alter. The TORREY CANYON oil spill in 1967 is a case in point. Heavy and inappropriate use of very toxic detergents (as distinct from dispersants) caused massive damage to some shores, and although re-colonisation by most of the dominant organisms was rapid, subtle differences in the distribution of species could be detected for more than ten years when compared with un-oiled sites.

The amenity value of beaches and rocky shores may call for the use of more rapid and aggressive clean-up techniques, which may damage plants and animals. On rocky shores, the use of dispersants or high pressure hot water washing and sand blasting may result in ecological damage greater than that caused by the oil. Cutting and removal of seaweed should only be done in cases of severe contamination and when movement of the oil to clean areas is a concern. Special care is needed during clean-up at the breeding sites of marine mammals, turtles and birds, to avoid causing disturbance.

- **Soft sediment shores**
  Soft sediment shores, consisting of fine sands and mud, are found in areas that are sheltered from wave action, such as estuaries, and tend to be highly biologically productive. They often support large populations of migrating birds, indigenous populations of specialist sediment dwellers and shell fisheries. They also act as nursery areas for some species. Oil can become incorporated into fine sediments through a number of mechanisms. Examples include flocculation, with sediment stirred up by storm activity, and penetration into worm burrows and open plant stems. If oil does penetrate fine sediments it can persist for many years, increasing the likelihood of longer-term effects.

■ **Oil penetrating into the substrate can remain for years**

### Saltmarshes

The upper fringes of 'soft' shores are often dominated by saltmarshes, which are characterised by dense low vegetation on mudflats drained by a network of channels. The organic input from the marsh provides the basic source of food for a rich and diverse fauna of worms, snails, clams and crabs that are in turn eaten by birds. Marsh vegetation shows greater sensitivity to lighter more penetrating oils, which are more likely to cause acute toxic damage than heavy or weathered oils. Oiling of the lower portion of plants and their root systems can be lethal, but a severe coating of oil on foliage may be of little consequence, particularly if it occurs outside of the growing season.

 **Typically, salt marshes are only temporarily harmed by a single oiling, but damage lasting many years can be inflicted by repeated spills or by aggressive clean-up activity, such as trampling or removal of contaminated substrate.**

### Mangroves

In tropical regions, mangrove swamps consisting of salt tolerant trees and bushes inhabit sheltered coasts and estuaries and provide a rich and diverse habitat as well as coastal protection and important nursery areas. Mangroves have complex root systems above the surface of the organically rich and oxygen depleted muds in which they live to enable them to breathe. They are known to be highly sensitive to the effects of oil spills, particularly heavy fuel oils, which can smother these root systems. Mangroves growing in fine sediments (muds) seem to be more susceptible than those in coarse grain sediments. Oil damages the mangroves either by blocking the openings of their air breathing roots or by interfering with the trees' salt balance, causing leaves to drop and the trees to die.

 **Where high mortality of trees that are 50 or more years old has occurred the re-establishment of a mature mangrove forest can take decades.**

■ **Mangroves are highly sensitive to oil spills and can be further damaged by many types of clean-up activity**

The physical removal of oil from a marsh or from within a mangrove forest is very difficult. The cleaning process also carries a risk of damaging the root systems of the plants, which perform a vital role in stabilising the mud substrate. Techniques such as low pressure water flushing and dispersants from boats are likely to be ineffective and impractical. The merits of cutting oiled vegetation and long-term restorative measures, such as replanting, must be viewed against the damage caused by trampling and disturbance.

### Corals

Coral reefs are found in shallow warm waters off most tropical coastlines and islands. Living coral grows on the calcified remains of dead coral colonies, which form overhangs, crevices and irregularities that are inhabited by a rich variety of fish and other animals. Many coral reefs are suffering degradation due to a variety of causes, including climate change, natural disturbances and fishing practices, as well as pollution.

Coral reefs are generally submerged and it is only when they are briefly exposed to air at low tide that they are vulnerable to physical coating by floating oil. Because of the turbulence and wave action characteristic of reefs, the corals may also be exposed to naturally dispersed oil droplets. The effects of oil on corals and their associated fauna are largely determined by the proportion of toxic components, the duration of oil exposure and the presence and severity of other stress factors.

Observations of oiled corals suggest that several sub-lethal effects may occur, such as interference with the reproductive process, abnormal behaviour and reduced or suspended growth. Most of the

■ **Oil spills may be one of a number of threats to the health of a coral reef**

effects are temporary, but similar impact on the associated reef fauna can have greater repercussions as narcotised animals may be swept away from the protection of the reef by waves and currents.

The waters over most reefs are shallow and turbulent and few clean-up techniques can be recommended. The possible benefits of mechanical recovery techniques are outweighed by the practical difficulties and potential physical damage caused by vessels and anchors. When current directions are favourable, dispersants may serve to protect coral reefs from wind-driven oil. However, caution should be observed, particularly when operating close to a reef.

### Seagrasses

Seagrasses are flowering plants that grow in shallow or sheltered coastal waters, anchored in sand or mud bottoms. They provide habitat and food for a variety of marine, estuarine and beach-dwelling animal species. Research into the effects of oil spills on seagrass is limited, but findings point to minimal impact on the plants themselves, although the effects on the populations of animals living on or between them are more noticeable. The use of dispersants may increase the exposure of submerged seagrasses to oil as dispersed oil enters the water column. Clean-up operations in the vicinity of seagrass should be undertaken with care as the plants can be torn or pulled out by vessel propellers and boom anchors.

## 5.2 Natural Recovery

Animals and plants have varying degrees of natural resilience to changes in their habitats. Natural adaptations, combined with breeding strategies, provide important mechanisms for coping with daily and seasonal fluctuations in habitats and for dealing with pressures from predation and other natural phenomena, such as hurricanes and tsunamis.

Protective mechanisms adopted by marine organisms to survive periods of natural stress, such as pounding waves, drying winds and high temperatures, can be beneficial in the event of an oil spill. For example, intertidal animals are generally only active when submerged by the tide and at other times are quiescent and will shut their shells, retreat into burrows and crevices or isolate themselves in some other way from the adverse conditions caused through exposure to air. These same mechanisms may help them to tolerate short-term coating by oil during low tide.

Another important strategy for many marine organisms is the production of vast numbers of eggs and larvae, which are released into the plankton and are widely distributed by currents. In some cases only one or two individuals in a million survive through to adulthood. This over-production of young stages ensures that there is a considerable reservoir not only for the colonisation of new areas, but also for the replacement of any adults that have been killed as a result of predation or some other calamity. Long-lived species, that do not reach sexual maturity for many years and which produce few offspring, are likely to take much longer to recover from the effects of an oil spill.

> In view of the natural variability of animal and plant populations, it is usually very difficult to assess the effects of an oil spill and to determine when a habitat has recovered to its pre-spill state.

There is considerable debate over what constitutes recovery; natural variability in systems makes getting back to the exact pre-spill condition unlikely. Most current definitions of recovery focus on the re-establishment of a community of plants and animals that are characteristic of the habitat and are functioning normally in terms of biodiversity and productivity.

## 5.3 Reinstatement

Sometimes practical measures can be taken to return the affected environment to normal conditions more quickly and effectively than through natural recovery processes alone. The first stage on the road to recovery is usually the removal of bulk oil contamination through a well conducted clean-up operation. For many marine habitats, the clean-up operation is all that is necessary to promote natural recovery and there is little more that can be done to speed up this process.

In some cases, however, particularly in circumstances where habitat recovery would otherwise be relatively slow, the clean-up operation can be followed by further measures that help restore a habitat structure. An example of such an approach would be to replant an area of saltmarsh or mangrove after the bulk oil contamination has been removed. In this way erosion of the area would be minimised and other forms of biological life would be encouraged to return.

While it may be possible to help restore damaged vegetation and physical structures, designing meaningful reinstatement strategies for animals is a much greater challenge. In some cases it may be warranted to protect a natural breeding population at a nearby non-impacted site, for example by predator control, to provide a reservoir from which re-colonisation of the impacted areas can occur.

Other examples include implementing controls on fishing where this represents competition for a limited food source, or closing beaches used as nesting sites for the season to minimise disturbance. In reality, the complexity of the marine environment means that there are limits to which ecological damage can be repaired by artificial means. In most cases natural recovery is likely to be relatively rapid and will rarely be outpaced by reinstatement measures.

## 5.4 Post-Spill Studies

To determine the full extent of the damage and the progress of the recovery, it may be necessary to undertake post-spill studies. The costs of post-spill studies may be admissible for compensation under international conventions provided they are a direct consequence of a particular spill and are intended to establish the precise nature and extent of environmental damage and habitat recovery.

Studies will not be necessary after all spills and would normally be most appropriate in the case of major incidents where there is evidence of significant environmental damage. Any studies considered should be carried out with scientific rigour, objectivity and balance, with the aim of providing reliable and useful information towards assessing pollution damage, reasonable reinstatement measures and habitat recovery. The scale of such studies should be in proportion to the extent of the contamination and the predictable effects.

The short-term effects of oil spills on many marine species and communities are well known and predictable but, for a variety of reasons not the least of which is funding, there are not many long-term studies from which to draw conclusions about possible longer term population effects. In those studies that have been undertaken, it is generally found that long-term impacts are conspicuous and related to the persistence of oil in a geographically discrete area. Although more subtle effects are postulated, it is difficult to attribute these definitively to a specific oil spill due to the confusing influence of other factors such as natural variability, climatic effects and other natural and manmade impacts.

---

**METULA – Strait of Magellan, Chile, 1974**

The tanker METULA grounded in the eastern Strait of Magellan, Chile, on 9 August 1974. About 47,000 tonnes of light Arabian crude oil and 3,000 to 4,000 tonnes of heavy fuel oil were estimated to have been lost. Large volumes of water-in-oil emulsion were produced in the rough sea conditions and much of this landed on shores of northern Tierra del Fuego. Most of the shores affected were of mixed sand and gravel, but two small estuaries including saltmarshes were also oiled. About 4,000 birds were known to have been killed, including cormorants and penguins.

No clean-up was done because of the remoteness of the area and so this remains a useful site for comparison and research, mainly because hard asphalt pavements (agglomerates of oil and pebbles) formed on many shorelines. The long-term fate and effects of heavy oiling along these shorelines have been extensively investigated. One very sheltered marsh received thick deposits of emulsion and, 20 years after the spill, these deposits were still visible on the marsh surface, with the emulsion quite fresh in appearance beneath a weathered surface skin. Little plant re-colonisation has occurred in the areas with thicker deposits of 4 cm or more, although it was proceeding in more lightly oiled areas. On sand and gravel shores, an asphalt pavement remained in a relatively sheltered area in 1998, but oil deposits had mainly broken up and disappeared from more exposed shores. These remain among the longest-term deposits of oil recorded from an oil spill, even though they have not resulted in significant impacts on fisheries or the biology of coastal waters.

# ECONOMIC EFFECTS OF OIL SPILLS 6

Oil spills can have a serious economic impact on coastal activities and on those who depend on the resources of the sea. Prominent among the activities affected are fishing and mariculture (the cultivation of marine species). Other sectors, such as tourism, shipping and industries that rely on seawater for their routine operations, can also suffer economic consequences. In addition, oil spills can result in physical damage to property or to local crops and livestock on adjacent coastlines. In most cases oil spill damage is temporary and is caused primarily by the physical properties of oil creating nuisance and hazardous conditions.

## 6.1 Fisheries and Mariculture

Oil spills can cause damage to fishing and mariculture resources by physical contamination, toxic effects and by disrupting business activity.

The nature and extent of the impact of an oil spill on seafood production depends on the characteristics of the spilt oil, the circumstances of the incident and the type of fishing activity or businesses affected.

■ A selection of seafood for sale at a Korean restaurant

**Physical contamination**
Oil can directly damage the boats and gear used for catching or cultivating marine species. Such contamination is then easily transferred to the catch, which may also become physically contaminated or may acquire an objectionable oil-derived taste known as 'tainting'.

Flotation equipment, lift nets, cast nets and fixed traps extending above the sea surface are most

likely to become contaminated by floating oil. Lines, dredges, bottom trawls and the submerged parts of cultivation facilities are usually well protected, provided they are not lifted through an oily sea surface or affected by sunken oil. Less common is the mortality of stock, which can be caused by physical contamination or close contact with freshly spilt oil in shallow waters with poor water exchange.

■ Fishing nets and other gear can be contaminated by oil

A precautionary ban on catching and sale of fish and shellfish in a particular area, both to maintain market confidence and to protect fishing gear and catches from contamination, may result in a temporary financial loss to fishermen. For subsistence fishermen, particularly in developing countries, it may also lead to temporary food shortages unless they are able to pursue alternative uncontaminated stocks or find other sources of income.

Cultivated stocks kept in cages or tanks are particularly vulnerable to oil spills as they are usually unable to avoid exposure to oil contaminants in the water, in which case effects, such as tainting and mortality, may be worsened. In addition, when fish farming facilities become physically coated with floating oil, their polluted surfaces may act as a source of stock re-contamination until they are cleaned.

■ Cultured stock, such as oysters, are particularly vulnerable to oil spills

Cultured seaweed is particularly vulnerable in tidal areas where it may become contaminated with oil at low tide. Seaweeds such as kelp are better protected because they are suspended from floating structures in deep water.

The cultivation of many marine species frequently involves the use of onshore tanks to rear the young to marketable size, or to a size and age suitable for transfer to the sea. Such facilities are usually supplied with clean sea water drawn through intakes located below the low water mark. The intakes may occasionally be under threat from sunken oil or dispersed oil droplets, which may lead to contamination of pipe work and tanks and the contamination of cultivated stock.

### Protection and clean-up techniques
Booms and other physical barriers can sometimes be used to protect fixed fishing gear and mariculture facilities, although in most cases it is impossible to prevent damage altogether. In calm conditions fish farms can sometimes be protected with heavy-duty plastic sheeting wrapped around the perimeter of the cages, thereby preventing floating oil from entering the nets or contaminating the floats.

Dispersants should be used with care so as not to cause tainting of shellfish and captured or cultivated stock. As a general guide, dispersants should not be used in shallow waters where fishing or mariculture is important. However, if used at a safe distance, dispersants can reduce or prevent contamination of equipment by floating oil.

■ **Weighted plastic sheeting suspended around fish cages to prevent contamination by floating oil**

Sorbent materials are often useful for removing oil sheens from water and tank surfaces. Sorbent booms are easy to deploy and move, and serve to control sheens in floating cultivation pens. However, oil-saturated sorbents should be replaced regularly to avoid them becoming a source of secondary pollution.

### Business interruption
The most serious threat from oil spills to fisheries and mariculture activity is the economic loss arising from business interruption. Oil on the water and the application of temporary fishing and harvesting bans may prevent normal production. A loss of market confidence may also occur, leading to price reductions or outright rejection of seafood products by commercial buyers and consumers. In extreme cases, the mere hint of oil contamination can affect the marketing of high price luxury seafood, even if the produce is proven to be taint free after testing. Mariculture operators tend to sell their produce intermittently and so the timing and duration of

harvesting bans in relation to the normal farming cycle will largely determine the extent of economic loss.

■ **A survey to assess the damage to seafood stocks**

It is almost always necessary to make a thorough investigation of the status of a fishery and alleged effects of a spill in order to determine the real impacts; this will often require scientifically rigorous sampling and analytical techniques. Separating spill effects from other factors that affect fisheries is frequently problematic. Wild stocks of commercial species are in decline in many parts of the world because of over-fishing, industrial pollution, destruction of coastal habitats and other natural factors such as increasing sea temperature. Similarly, mariculture is often ravaged by disease or suffers from the accumulation of its own wastes. Therefore, to make the best assessment of damages attributable to contamination by oil, it is necessary to make comparisons of post spill recovery results with the conditions that pre-existed the spill or with control areas outside of the affected area.

It is sometimes suggested that fish and shellfish stocks will be depleted for a number of years after a spill because of damage to eggs and larvae. However, experience from major spills has shown that the possibility of such long-term effects is remote as the normal overproduction of eggs provides a reservoir to compensate for any localised losses. Furthermore, temporary harvesting bans may actually boost wild stocks, particularly those subject to over-fishing.

### Tainting
The contamination of seafood can usually be detected as a petroleum taste or taint. Taint is commonly defined as an odour or flavour that is foreign to a food product and oil tainted food is generally unpalatable, even at very low levels of contamination. Species with a high fat content in the flesh, such as salmon and herring, have a greater tendency than lean muscle species to accumulate and retain petroleum hydrocarbons in their tissues.

The presence and persistence of taint will depend mainly on the type and fate of oil, the species affected, the extent of exposure, hydrographic conditions and temperature. Tainting of living tissue is reversible but, whereas the uptake of oil taint is frequently rapid (minutes or hours), the depuration process whereby contaminants are metabolised and eliminated from the organism is slower (weeks).

One of the main concerns about tainting is the possible public health hazard of eating products contaminated by oil-derived compounds, which may include low levels of carcinogens. Most studies, however, have led to the conclusion that eating seafood from areas where oil spills have occurred is not a significant threat to public health, even for subsistence consumers. Nevertheless, public confidence in seafood products can quickly erode as a result of suspect, or actually contaminated, products reaching the market.

Properly conducted sensory testing is an efficient and appropriate method for establishing the presence and disappearance of tainting and for indicating whether seafood is fit for human consumption. This requires trained taste panels and valid control samples. Tests are conducted 'blind'; this is where the testers do not know the identity of either the control or the potentially tainted samples. Confidence in accepting that the fish or shellfish are clean and safe following a particular spill comes from an adequately timed series of monitored data showing the progressive reduction in taint.

---

**AEGEAN SEA – Spain, 1992**

On 3 December 1992, the Greek OBO carrier (ore/bulk/oil) AEGEAN SEA ran aground during heavy weather while approaching the port of La Coruna on the Galician coast, North West Spain. The vessel broke in two and caught fire, spilling an estimated 74,000 tonnes of North Sea Brent crude in an area famed for its fisheries and mariculture resources. Much of the oil either dispersed at sea or was consumed by the fire onboard the vessel, but spilt crude oil also impacted rocky shores, small sandy beaches and a salt marsh/mud flat area. The Galician Fisheries Council deliberately authorised and encouraged fishermen to exceed published daily quotas of shellfish in an area under threat from spreading oil, but as yet unaffected, thereby reducing the anticipated loss of production. By this prompt action, the economic effects on the fishermen were reduced. A harvesting ban was imposed that lasted eight months, but fishermen were still able to obtain their full annual quota in the remaining four months of the year because the shellfish stocks were non-migratory and available for collection in larger numbers of bigger specimens when the ban was lifted.

There were also extensive mariculture facilities for mussels in the area. Physical contamination of the farms was slight, but significant tainting of mussels occurred through exposure to dispersed oil droplets. A ban was imposed on all mariculture activity for over a year, leading to mussel farming losses estimated at over $6 million. The effect of the ban on all cultivation and maintenance activity was to remove any possibility of depurated mussels ever reaching the market. Some 8,000 tonnes of mussels were condemned and destroyed at a municipal waste site. When the ban was lifted in May 1994, mussel cultivation resumed with the collection of fresh seedlings. The Fisheries Council justified the drastic intervention as a means of protecting seafood product image.

---

Due to a lack of trained taste panels, chemical analysis is now used more frequently to screen fish and shellfish for taint. This is most commonly undertaken using gas chromatography linked to mass spectrometry (GC/MS) to measure PAH (polycyclic aromatic hydrocarbon) concentrations. These are then compared with nationally or internationally accepted standards or with levels found in reference samples taken from a local control area.

## 6.2 Tourism

■ **Manual clean-up on a tourist beach**

Polluted shorelines are a common feature of many major oil spills, leading to public alarm and interference with traditional coastal activities such as bathing, boating, angling, diving and bird watching. Hotel and restaurant owners, sailing schools, aquariums, caravan parks and the many other business and individuals who gain their livelihood from the tourist trade can be affected as visitors shorten or cancel their stays. Because of their visual impact, persistent oils and their residues cause the most nuisance and concern, particularly if the incident occurs just before or during the main tourist season.

 The disturbance from a single oil spill to coastal areas and to recreational pursuits will be comparatively short-lived and, after clean-up, public confidence is more likely to require rebuilding.

Once shorelines are clean, normal trade and activity would be expected to resume, although media attention may cause disproportionate damage to the image of the local tourist industry, aggravating economic losses by contributing to a public perception of prolonged and widescale pollution. This could result, for example, in bookings being lost even by hotels and other businesses outside of the affected area. The degradation of the 'brand image' of a region may call for targeted regional advertising campaigns and other promotional activities to counteract negative publicity generated by the spill.

## 6.3 Property Damage

Oil spills can result in physical damage to property, for example, through contaminating fishing gear, as previously mentioned, or oiling pleasure boats and other vessels. Shipyards with slipways and dry docks used for construction and repair work may also be affected by oil spills, causing damage to unpainted or newly painted surfaces and creating hazardous working conditions.

### Vessel Cleaning

Oil stains on vessel hulls are typically limited to a band around the waterline. Hulls can usually be cleaned while still in the water if undertaken with minimal delay. Inducing a list in the vessel, thereby exposing the waterline, may allow oil to be removed with rags and one of a range of proprietary vessel cleaning products stocked by yacht chandlers. To avoid secondary pollution runoff should be recovered, for example by a sorbent boom surrounding the work area. Some cleaning products may damage hull coatings and a small test area should be tried first. Concerns about product toxicity also mean that the use of cleaning agents may be controlled by local regulations.

For more intractable stains, vessels may be slipped or hauled out for cleaning and stronger cleaning agents used. However, some agents, such as those based on chlorine, ammonia, acetone or ketones, may damage the gel coat of fibreglass vessels.

The severity of staining depends on a number of factors, including the oil characteristics and degree of contamination, the time that the oil is left in place and the type and condition of the hull coating. Older and more porous coatings are likely to be penetrated more easily and, therefore, stained more heavily than newer ones. Some coatings are finished with a wax polish, which is likely to be removed by the oil, while polymer based top coats are more resilient.

An area may be established within a marina or harbour where vessels can be cleaned either by their owners or by a contactor engaged specifically for the task. Cleaned and oiled vessels should be separated to prevent the risk of re-oiling. If vessels are to be lifted out of the water, the hire of a specialised crane may be required.

In many marinas the vessels are moored to floating walkways. If oiled, these can be cleaned with high pressure, hot water equipment. On rare occasions the walkways may have to be dismantled to allow the floats to be cleaned to prevent secondary pollution.

■ **Steam cleaning a boat to remove oil stains**

During some incidents, oil is carried ashore as airborne oil particles, contaminating houses, caravans and cars, which may then require cleaning, repair or repainting. Trees and shrubs may also be damaged by the wind blown oil and need replacing.

The rapid restoration of a contaminated area may call for the use of highly effective clean-up techniques, but at the same time these may be harmful to property. Seawalls, harbours and other manmade structures can be affected by severe measures such as sand blasting, and increased heavy vehicle traffic may damage local roads. In selecting a clean-up technique, it is necessary to strike a balance between effectiveness and possible additional damage.

## 6.4 Industry

Industries that rely on a supply of clean sea water for their normal operations can also be adversely affected by oil spills. Power stations, in particular, are often located close to the coast to have access to the very large quantities of water required for cooling purposes. A total shutdown or a reduction in output will be required if substantial quantities of floating or subsurface oil are drawn through intakes, contaminating the condenser tubes. Similarly, the normal operation of desalination plants may be disrupted by oil, causing water supply problems for consumers.

■ **Boom deployed as a precautionary measure to protect power station water intakes**

Shipping may be disrupted by a spill and subsequent clean-up operations, particularly if the incident occurs in a harbour or port approach. The deployment of booms or closure of lock gates to contain oil may cause delays. Direct contamination of jetties as well as mooring lines and ships' waterlines is a common occurrence and oil may become trapped under and around other ships that are moored in the area. There is also a risk of oil entrainment in shipboard condenser tubes causing damage to boilers and evaporators; this latter problem is comparatively rare, probably because of the depths of the seawater intakes below the sea surface and the relatively low flow rates. As industrial ports are among the locations most at risk from spills, they are often well prepared for clean-up, with response equipment close at hand.

■ **Spills within port limits can be disruptive to commercial activities**

Other routine harbour activities, such as ferry services, lock operations and towage, can be disrupted, particularly after a spill of light crude oil, gasoline or other flammable substance.

Welding and the use of spark generating machinery may have to be suspended as long as a fire hazard persists. In this way, even small spills in a busy port can have considerable repercussions.

Salt production is another industry that may be adversely affected by an oil spill. In regions with limited rainfall, salt may be produced by the evaporation of sea water in salt pans along the coast. Production facilities range from artisanal, with salt pans dug out of mud in salt marshes, to industrial scale, with glazed tile ponds and pumped water supplies. Sea water is generally only drawn into the ponds at high water during spring tides and the flow into the ponds is controlled by sluice gates. In the event of a spill, oil can sometimes be prevented from entering the ponds simply by closing the sluice gates. If pollution is prolonged, it may be possible to maintain production by allowing seawater into the ponds through filters constructed from sorbents and shells and by careful monitoring of water quality.

■ **The production of salt can be severely affected if an oil spill occurs when water is let into the pans**

## 6.5 Agriculture

Another sector that may feel the economic consequences of an oil spill is the farming community. In certain circumstances, oil can be blown from the coastline onto arable and grazing land. Crops may have to be destroyed or fertilizers applied to enhance the recovery of the land by

accelerating the natural breakdown of the oil. As a precautionary measure, farmers and crofters may be advised to remove livestock from the affected area until the implications of the apparent contamination can be assessed, incurring various additional labour costs and other expenses. As a result of a spill, the integrity and image of the local produce may suffer, causing a drop in sales and reduction in income.

---

**BRAER – Shetland, UK, 1993**

An unusual feature of the BRAER incident in January 1993 was that a significant amount of oil was blown onto land adjacent to the wreck site by severe and persistent gale force winds. At the height of the incident almost 60 square kilometres of land were coated with a fine layer of oil. Two weeks of rain and high winds following the spill reduced the visible level of contamination considerably and most of the oil detected on vegetation during the release of the BRAER's cargo was no longer present by the end of the month. There was concern about the effects of oil on crops, grazing sheep and cattle and measures were taken to safeguard human food chains and the health of livestock. Because of a lack of information on the impact of hydrocarbons on livestock, farmers and crofters were advised to remove out-wintering animals from the affected area and, in total, some 23,000 sheep were moved from their normal grazing and given special feed while the implications of the oiling were assessed. As a further precautionary measure, crops such as turnips and cabbages from the affected area were declared unfit for human consumption. Monitoring work was quickly launched and it was demonstrated that the effects of the airborne oil were localised and had no more than a temporary impact on vegetation and livestock.

---

> The primary reasons for a rapid response to a spill are to return activities to normal as quickly as possible and to minimise the risk of oil contaminating environmentally or aesthetically important areas.

---

## 6.6 Compensation for Economic Loss

Those who are placed at a financial disadvantage as a result of an oil spill may be entitled to compensation under applicable international conventions. In the case of a spill of persistent oil from a tanker, a system exists whereby both tanker owners and oil cargo receivers (primarily oil companies) contribute to the payment of compensation up to about $1.2 billion, according to the terms of the 1992 Civil Liability Convention (1992 CLC), the 1992 Fund Convention and its 2003 Protocol (Supplementary Fund). The conventions apply in any state that chooses to ratify them, irrespective of the owner and flag of the tanker or the owner of the cargo. Most claims are settled promptly without the need for litigation because the liability of tanker owners is 'strict', i.e. there is no need to prove fault.

Compensation may also be available for those who suffer damage caused by spills of oil carried as fuel by non-tankers under the International Convention on Civil Liability for Bunker Oil Pollution Damage.

Some countries that have not ratified the international compensation conventions have their own domestic legislation for compensating those affected by spills of oil and other substances from ships. Some of these may be highly specific, such as the Oil Pollution Act of 1990 in the USA, while other countries may rely on broader laws originally developed for other purposes.

Further information on presenting claims for compensation can be found in ITOPF's Technical Information Paper 'Preparedness and Submission of Claims for Oil Pollution' and the International Oil Pollution Compensation Fund 1992 Claims Manual.

■ **Oiled fishing boats – reasonable costs of cleaning, repairing or replacing property that has been contaminated by oil are likely to be compensable under the applicable international liability and compensation regimes**

# CONTAINMENT AND RECOVERY 7

When oil is spilt at sea, attempts are usually made to contain and recover the oil in an effort to reduce the threat to shorelines. The most common approach is to use floating barriers, or booms, to halt or minimise the spread of the oil and to concentrate it into a thicker layer that can be recovered with a pump or skimmer.

## 7.1 Containment

Commercially available booms are the most common form of barrier used in oil spill control. They are designed to perform one or more of the following functions:

**Oil containment and concentration**
Surrounding floating oil to reduce its spread and increase the thickness of an oil layer in order to facilitate recovery.

**Deflection**
Diverting oil to a suitable collection point on the shoreline for subsequent removal by vacuum trucks, pumps or other recovery methods.

**Protection**
Preventing oil from entering economically important or biologically sensitive sites, such as harbour entrances, power station cooling water intakes, fish farms or nature reserves.

■ **Inflatable boom containing oil around a partially submerged wreck**

■ **Boom used as a spur to deflect oil to the shore for recovery**

■ **Fence boom protecting a marina**

### 7.1.1 Boom Design

Booms come in a variety of sizes, materials and designs to meet the demands of differing environments and situations. They can range from cheap, lightweight models for manual deployment in harbours up to large, robust units for offshore use, which may require cranes and sizeable vessels to handle them. With some designs, skimmers are incorporated into the face of the boom, providing a combined containment and recovery system. Booms are available in a variety of lengths, with couplings to allow sections to be combined to the desired overall length. Couplings also provide towing and anchoring points. A variety of ancillary equipment, such as reels, towing bridles and air blowers, may be required.

All booms normally incorporate the following features:

- Freeboard to prevent or reduce splashover

- subsurface skirt to prevent or reduce escape of oil under the boom

- flotation by air, foam or other buoyant material

- longitudinal tension member (chain or wire) to withstand effects of winds, waves and currents

- ballast to maintain the vertical aspect of the boom.

Their design falls into two broad categories:

- Fence booms, which generally have a flat cross-section held vertically in the water by integral or external buoyancy and bracing struts

- curtain booms, which provide a continuous subsurface skirt or flexible screen supported by an air or foam filled flotation chamber, usually of circular cross-section.

Additional types include:

- Shore sealing boom, where the skirt is replaced by water filled chambers, allowing the boom to settle on an exposed shoreline at low tide

- fire boom, which is either of a fence or curtain design, but is specifically constructed to withstand the high temperatures generated by burning oil.

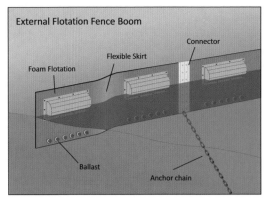

■ An external flotation fence boom with external flotation and ballast; mooring points are located at intervals along its lower length

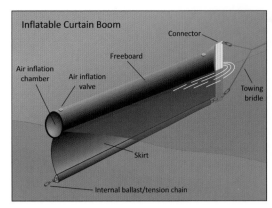

■ An inflatable curtain boom with a combined ballast and tension chain fitted in an integral pocket attached to the bottom of the skirt

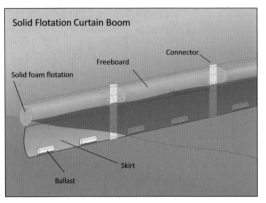

■ A solid flotation curtain boom with external ballast

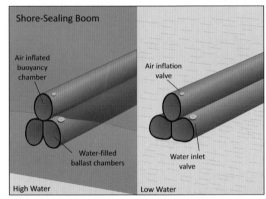

■ Intertidal shore sealing boom; upper air inflation pocket to allow flotation, lower water filled pockets to provide ballast when floating and to ensure a good seal with the substrate at low tide

| Type of Boom | Flotation Method | Storage | Wave Following Property | Moored or Towed? | Ease of Cleaning | Relative Cost | Preferred Use |
|---|---|---|---|---|---|---|---|
| Curtain Boom | Inflatable | Compact when deflated | Good | Both | Straightforward | High | Inshore or offshore |
| | Solid foam | Bulky | Reasonable | Moored | Easy/Straight-forward | Mid range | Sheltered inshore waters e.g. harbours |
| Fence Boom | External foam floats | Bulky | Poor | Moored | Difficult/Medium; oil can become trapped behind external floatation or in the junctions of the chambers | Low | Sheltered waters (e.g. ports, marinas) |
| Shore-Sealing Boom | Inflatable upper chamber, lower chambers water filled | Compact when deflated | Good | Moored | Medium; oil can become trapped in junction of the chambers | High | Along sheltered intertidal shores (no breaking waves) |

■ Table 7.1: Characteristics of common boom types

## 7.1.2   Boom Characteristics

**The most important characteristic of a boom is its oil containment or deflection capability, determined by its behaviour in relation to water movement.**

A boom should be flexible to conform to wave motion, yet sufficiently rigid to retain as much oil as possible. Some designs of fence boom, in particular, exhibit poor wave following characteristics, causing the freeboard to sink below the surface or the skirt to ride between crests as a wave passes, allowing oil to escape. This type of boom should be limited to use in calm waters.

Other important boom characteristics are strength, ease and speed of deployment, reliability, weight and cost, see Table 7.1. It is essential that a boom is sufficiently robust and durable for its intended purpose as it will often need to tolerate inexpert handling, twisting, large and heavy floating debris and abrasion from rocks, dock walls or coral. Structural strength is required particularly to withstand the forces of water and wind when it is either towed or moored. Ease and speed of deployment, combined with reliability, are clearly very important in a rapidly changing situation.

### 7.1.3   Boom Failures

The way in which oil escapes, and its relation with water velocity, is as much a function of oil type as boom design, see Figure 7.1.

- Viscous oils escape faster than non-viscous oils, tending to accumulate at the boom face and to flow vertically down and under the skirt. This is termed drainage failure ①

- low viscosity oils take longer to escape as they are carried under the boom as droplets, sheared from the underside of the oil layer by turbulence in the headwave. This is termed entrainment failure ②

- in choppy seas, oil can splash over the boom's freeboard. Splash-over can also occur as a result of extensive oil accumulation in the boom ③.

Other common boom failures include:

Submergence – strong currents or too high towing speeds may cause the boom to submerge, particularly if the buoyancy of the boom is too low.

Planing – this occurs when a combination of wind in one direction and a strong current in the other forces the boom to lie flat on the water surface, or even to lift.

### 7.1.4   Boom Performance

Although some boom systems have been developed for use in fast flowing water and others for towing at relatively high speeds, most conventional boom designs are not capable of containing oil against water velocities much in excess of 0.5 ms⁻¹ (1 knot) acting at right angles to it. In practice, the escape velocity for most booms is around 0.35 ms⁻¹ (0.7 knots) irrespective of skirt depth.

**'Buster' Technology**
The Current Buster™ is one of a series of inflatable boom systems designed to work in currents or at tow speeds in excess of the 0.5 ms⁻¹ (1 knot) limit of conventional booms. It incorporates a flexible 'V' shaped surface boom that is towed between two vessels or alongside one. Oil is corralled down to the end of the 'V', where a separator removes it from the water. The oil can then be recovered by a simple pump or a conventional skimmer. The system showed favourable results in tests and has also been successfully deployed during actual oil spills ranging from diesel to heavy fuel oil.

Image courtesy of NOFI/Allmaritim

■ **NOFI Current Buster™, designed for use in tow speeds of up to 2 ms⁻¹ (4 knots)**

The size and length of boom sections are important considerations. The optimum size of a boom is largely related to the sea state in which it is to be used. As a general rule, the minimum height of freeboard to prevent oil splash-over should be selected. The depth of skirt should be of similar dimensions. Too high a freeboard may cause problems of windage, where the freeboard acts as a sail. Increasing the depth of the skirt can make the boom more prone to drainage failure due to the increasing velocity of water passing under the boom.

Short sections can make booms easier to handle and can protect the integrity of the boom as a whole should one section fail, but these advantages must be weighed against the inconvenience

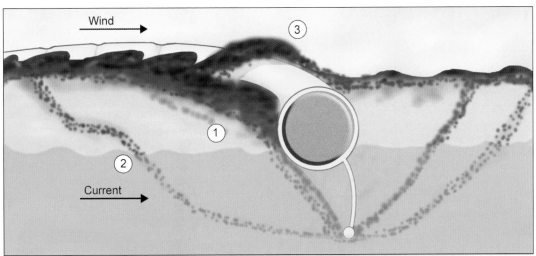

■ **Figure 7.1: Escape of oil from a boom**
       1. Drainage failure    2. Entrainment failure    3. Splash-over

and difficulty of connecting sections effectively. Connections interrupt the boom profile and, wherever possible, should not coincide with the point of heaviest oil concentrations. The design of connectors should allow easy fastening and unfastening during deployment and with the boom in the water. The many designs available can cause difficulties when joining booms from different sources.

## 7.1.5    Forces Exerted on Booms

To estimate the approximate force F (kg) exerted on a boom with a subsurface area A (m$^2$) by a current with velocity V (ms$^{-1}$), the following formula can be used:

$$F = 100 \times A \times V^2$$

Therefore, the force acting on a 100 m length of boom, with a 0.6 m skirt in a 0.25 ms$^{-1}$ (0.5 knot) water flow, would be:

$$F = 100 \times (0.6 \times 100) \times (0.25)^2 = 375 \text{ kg (force)}$$

It can be seen that doubling the current velocity would entail a four-fold increase in load. The force exerted by wind directly on the freeboard of the boom (windage) can also be considerable. To estimate the windage the above formula can be used on the basis that roughly equivalent pressures are created by a water current and a wind speed 40 times greater. For example, the approximate force on a 100 m length of boom with a 0.5 metre freeboard in a 7.5 ms$^{-1}$ (15 knot) wind would be:

$$F = 100 \times (0.5 \times 100) \times \left(\frac{7.5}{40}\right)^2 = 175 \text{ kg (force)}$$

In the above examples the combined forces of current and wind would be 550 kg if they were acting in the same direction on a rigid barrier. In practice, the boom is usually positioned at an angle to the flow, forming a curve, thereby modifying the magnitude and direction of the forces. However, these calculations provide a guide to the forces and are an aid to the selection of moorings or towing vessels. When a boom is towed its velocity through the water should be entered as the velocity 'V' in the formula set out in the beginning of this section.

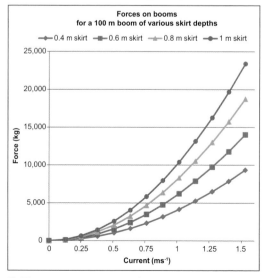

■ **Figure 7.2: Forces exerted on a 100 metre length of boom of various skirt depths, showing an exponential rise with increasing current**

## 7.1.6    Towed Booms

**The rapid spread of oil spilt at sea over a large area poses the most serious problem in attempting to contain floating oil using towed booms.**

To prevent spreading and to maximise encounter rate, long booms of 300 m or more can be towed in a 'U', 'V' or 'J' configuration using two vessels. In this way a swath up to 100 m wide can be achieved. The collection device is either towed with the boom array or deployed from a third vessel behind the boom. See Figure 7.3.

The most effective boom designs incorporate tension members, separated from the boom fabric either by an array of bridles or by a section of netting beneath the skirt. These arrangements encourage the boom to remain upright under tow and leave it free to adapt to wave motion.

■ **Inflatable boom deployed in a 'U' configuration between two vessels to contain a heavy crude oil**

Oil is most likely to escape beneath the inflexible connectors between boom sections. When towing a sectioned boom in a 'U' configuration, an odd number of sections of boom should be used so that there is not a join in the centre where oil is heaviest.

To avoid sharp strain or snatching on a towed boom, booms should not be attached directly to towing vessels. Instead, lines of sufficient length between boom ends and the vessel should be used. Lines of 50 m or more would be appropriate for towing a 300 m length of boom.

Boom performance can be judged at the apex of the 'U' or 'J' by eye. Oil lost under the boom will appear as globules or droplets rising behind the boom. Sheen may be present even when the boom is functioning well. Eddies behind the boom are an indication that it is being towed too fast.

To maximise performance, vessels should be able to maintain both the correct configuration of the towed booms and the desired very low speeds through the water, i.e. less than the escape velocity of the oil. Not only will each of the two towing vessels need at least half the total power required to tow the boom at the maximum speed consistent with oil retention, they will also need maximum manoeuvrability at slow speeds. Twin propulsion units, bow and stern thrusters and variable pitch

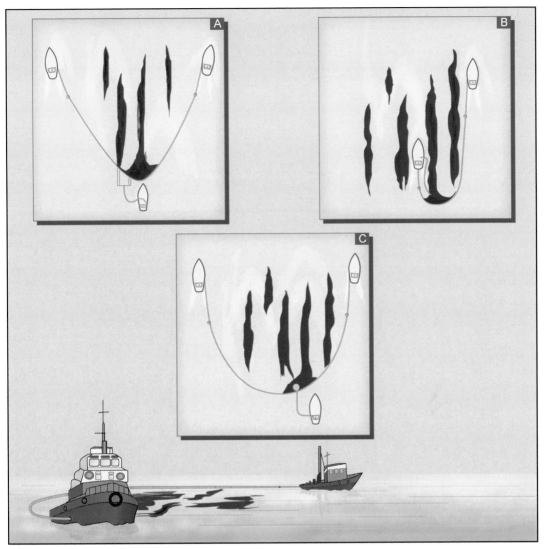

■ **Figure 7.3: a)** V configuration towed by two vessels — collection device towed with boom array and oil transferred to third vessel.
**b)** J configuration towed by two vessels, one of which deploys a collection device.
**c)** U configuration towed by two vessels — collection device deployed from a third vessel.

propellers are useful. An open and low aft deck working area with winch, lifting gear or a boom reel is necessary when handling bulky and heavy booms.

The ideal towing point aboard the vessel will need to be found by experiment and may need to be altered according to the course and wind direction. For example, a single screw vessel towing from the stern will not be very manoeuvrable and so towing from a forward point of the ship is preferable.

Good communication between the two towing vessels must be maintained so that both move at the same speed and in a controlled and coordinated manner. Aircraft equipped with air-to-sea communications could also be used to coordinate the movement and activities of vessels and to direct them to the thickest areas of oil.

Helicopters have the advantage of being able to hover over a thick patch of oil to verify and mark its location and can operate from a base close to the spill. Suitable recovery devices and sufficient onboard storage are also crucial to the overall success of the operation.

### 7.1.7 Moored Booms

In some circumstances it may be appropriate to anchor boom to contain spilt oil quite close to a source such as a leaking tanker or an offshore oil well. However, waters are sometimes too exposed and currents too strong for fixed booms to be effective. Even in calm conditions large instantaneous discharges of oil can easily swamp a boom, rendering it ineffective.

Placing booms close to the source may create a fire hazard and interfere with salvage activities or attempts to stem the flow of oil. The use of booms is also inappropriate in situations where the oil will dissipate naturally.

The main reason to use booms close to the shore is to protect particularly sensitive areas such as estuaries, marshes, mangroves, amenity areas and water intakes. Careful planning should be devoted to identifying and prioritising the areas that can be boomed effectively as, in practice, it may not be possible to protect all sites. A further advantage of planning is that preparations can be made for boom selection, mooring and oil collection. Planning is particularly relevant for oil terminals and similar installations where both the source and most likely size of spill can be predicted.

■ **Curtain boom deployed in front of a power station cooling water intake**

An aerial survey can be valuable when identifying suitable sites for using booms, including access points. When selecting the location and method of deployment it may be necessary to compromise between conflicting requirements. For instance, although it may be desirable to protect an entire river, the estuary may be too wide or the currents too strong to achieve this. A more suitable location may have to be sought further upstream bearing in mind the need for access to deploy the boom and remove the collected oil. If the oil is not removed at the rate of its arrival it will accumulate and move out towards the centre of the river, where the stronger currents may sweep the oil under the boom.

It is often better to use booms to deflect oil to relatively quiet waters, where it may be recovered, rather than attempt containment. As shown in Table 7.2, by angling the boom it is feasible to deflect floating oil even in a 1.5 ms$^{-1}$ (3 knot) current, where a boom positioned at right angles to the flow would fail to contain any oil. Following this principle, a river can be protected by placing a boom obliquely to the direction of flow. If it is necessary to maintain a navigation channel, two sections of boom can be staggered from opposite banks taking into account reversal of tidal flow.

| Current Strength | | Max. Angle |
|---|---|---|
| ms$^{-1}$ | (knots) | (degrees) |
| 0.35 | 0.7 | 90 |
| 0.5 | 1.0 | 45 |
| 0.75 | 1.5 | 28 |
| 1.0 | 2.0 | 20 |
| 1.25 | 2.5 | 16 |
| 1.5 | 3.0 | 13 |

■ **Table 7.2: Maximum boom deployment angle to flow direction at different current strengths to prevent escape of oil. Calculations based on an escape velocity of 0.35 m/s$^{-1}$ (0.7 knots) at 90°**

| Anchor Weight (kg) | Holding Strength (kg Force) | | |
|---|---|---|---|
| | Mud | Sand | Clay |
| 15 | 200 | 250 | 300 |
| 25 | 350 | 400 | 500 |
| 35 | 600 | 700 | 700 |

■ **Table 7.3: Holding strengths of Danforth type anchors in loose mud, sand or gravel, and clay**

Correct mooring of the boom is crucial as its performance depends on the angle of deflection remaining appropriate to the prevailing current strength. To maintain this angle and prevent the formation of pockets, frequent anchoring points may be required. However, the laying of multiple moorings is often impractical in an emergency. The formula to determine forces in Section 7.1.5 can be used, together with Tables 7.2 and 7.3, as a guide to the moorings required to hold a boom in a current of known strength and taking the likely maximum wind effect into account.

Types of anchors to be considered are:

- Danforth type anchor, which is effective on sand and mud substrates

- fisherman's type hook anchor, which is better on rocky bottoms

- concrete blocks; these can be cast to provide convenient and reliable mooring points, but their weight in air must be at least three times the expected load to compensate for their greater buoyancy in sea water.

■ **Danforth anchor**

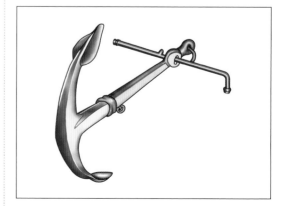

■ **Fisherman's anchor**

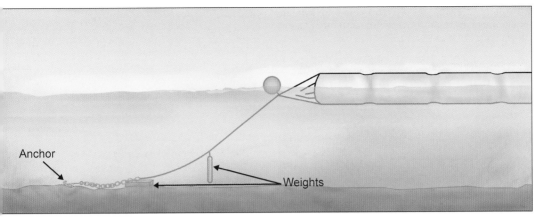

■ **Figure 7.4: Typical boom mooring arrangement. The same system would be employed at regular intervals along the boom**

The use of a workboat with lifting gear would be required to handle heavy moorings.

Whichever type of mooring is used, it is important to select the length of the mooring lines to suit the expected water depth, swell and tidal range. If the lines are too short the boom will not ride well in the water and the snatching produced in the lines by waves may dislodge the moorings or damage the boom. Conversely, if the lines are too long it will be difficult to control the configuration. A length of heavy chain or other weight between the anchor and line greatly improves the holding power of an anchor. The use of an intermediate buoy between the boom and anchor will help prevent submersion of the end of the boom. Similarly, a weight hung from the mooring lines stops them floating on the surface when slack, see Figure 7.4.

Booms can be directly attached to the hull of a ship using specially designed magnets. Magnets also have applications during salvage operations, as anchor points for divers for example, or temporary fixing points for tools and equipment.

■ **A sliding tidal compensator permits the boom to rise and fall with the tide**

For booms attached to fixed points, such as a wall or post along a jetty, sliding tidal compensators allow ready vertical movement of the boom, preventing oil bypassing the boom when water levels rise and fall.

When deploying a boom from a shoreline it is often possible to make use of fixed objects on the shore, such as trees or rocks. On a featureless shoreline multiple stakes or a buried object, such as a log, provide an excellent mooring point. Water ballasted shore-sealing booms are most suitable for deployment in this environment as their design enables containment throughout the tidal cycle. However, care should be taken in positioning these booms prior to ballasting as they are difficult to move on land once filled.

As winds, currents and tides change, so will the configuration of a boom. Frequent checks and re-adjustment of the moorings will be necessary and contained oil and debris must be removed promptly or the performance and benefit of the boom will be severely reduced.

In conditions where the air temperature is hot by day and cool by night, it is important to allow for the expansion and contraction of air in inflatable booms. This may necessitate letting air out during the day and re-inflating at night.

> It should be recognised that booms are vulnerable to damage by passing vessels, particularly at night, and it can be appropriate to take some precautions such as notifying mariners and displaying warning lights. Brightly coloured booms are more visible in daylight and are better picked out by lights at night.

As well as using booms to intercept or deflect oil they can be used in sheltered areas where oil has collected naturally to prevent it moving should conditions change. This not only minimises the extent of the contamination but also permits the controlled removal of the trapped oil.

Booms can also assist shoreline clean-up by containing the oil that is washed off beaches and rocks. By drawing in the boom the oil can be concentrated and moved toward collection devices.

■ **Semi-solid oil held against the shoreline by a section of inflatable boom to facilitate recovery**

## 7.1.8   Care and Maintenance of Booms

Some low cost booms are designed for single use, after which they can be incinerated or returned to the manufacturers for recycling, but many of the more expensive, robust booms, if properly deployed and maintained, can be reused time and time again. Booms usually require cleaning after use and this can prove difficult for some designs. Steam cleaning or solvents are usually employed, but when using the latter it is important to ensure that the boom fabric is compatible with such chemicals.

Proper retrieval, maintenance and storage are important to prolong the life of a boom and ensure that it is always ready for use at short notice. Some booms, particularly self-inflating models, are prone to damage from abrasion unless carefully retrieved. Emergency repair kits should be kept on hand for dealing with minor damage, which could otherwise make a section, or even the whole length, of boom unusable. Major damage to boom fabric is often difficult to repair and may necessitate replacement of the whole section.

Correct storage of booms is important to minimise long-term degradation of the boom material by high temperatures, UV light rays or mildew, although this is generally less of a problem with more advanced materials such as polyurethane or neoprene. Air flotation booms take up only a small storage area when deflated, whereas solid flotation booms are bulky. This should be considered when transporting booms to site and if storage is at a premium, such as on board a vessel.

■ **Oil trapped behind external floats of a fence boom can be particularly difficult to clean**

## 7.1.9   Limitations of Booms

The use of booms to contain and concentrate floating oil prior to its recovery is often seen as the ideal solution to a spill since, if effective, it would remove the oil from the marine environment. Unfortunately, this approach suffers from a number of fundamental problems, not least of which is the fact that it is in direct opposition to the natural tendency of the oil to spread, fragment and disperse under the influence of wind, waves and currents. In rough seas, a large spill of a low viscosity oil such as a light or medium crude oil can be scattered over many square kilometres within just a few hours. In addition, the deployment of booms can be a difficult and potentially hazardous operation.

> 💧 **Poor weather and rough seas impose limitations on operations. The handling of wet and oily equipment on vessels that are pitching and rolling is demanding and can place personnel at risk.**

On some occasions, the conditions may prevent the use of booms altogether and even in ideal, calm conditions it is important that operations are well planned and controlled, with a suitable strategy developed at the contingency planning stage.

## 7.1.10   Alternative Containment Systems

### Bubble barriers
The main disadvantage of any solid boom is that it may block the paths of boats and ships as well as oil. One solution to this problem is a bubble barrier. These are permanent installations that are in place to protect harbours where currents are relatively low and where there is high traffic flow. A rising curtain of bubbles is produced when air is pumped into a perforated pipe located below the water surface. The air bubbles create a counter-current on the water surface that holds the oil against a water flow of up to 0.35 ms$^{-1}$ (0.7 knots).

Their effectiveness is limited to thin layers of oil in calm and sheltered conditions as even a slight wind can cause oil to escape. Even simple systems require

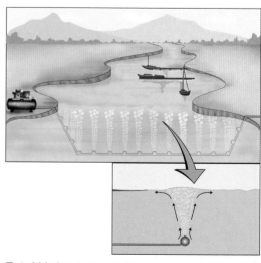

■ **Bubble barrier created by compressed air pumped through a submerged pipe with openings at regular intervals**

substantial compressors to make them effective. Checks of such systems are essential to ensure the air holes do not become blocked by silt or marine organisms.

## Improvised booms

When purpose built equipment is unavailable, it is possible to contain or collect oil successfully with improvised systems made with locally available materials. Alternatives to moored booms can be constructed from wood, oil drums, inflated fire hoses, rubber tyres or fishing nets filled with straw. In shallow waters, stakes may be driven into the bottom to support screens or mats made from sacking, reeds, bamboo or other such materials. On long sandy beaches, sand bars can be built out into shallow water with bulldozers to intercept oil moving along the shoreline. A similar approach can sometimes be used to prevent oil entering narrow estuaries or lagoons. If necessary, a measure of

■ **Improvised boom made from straw and palm fronds wrapped with sorbent pads**

water exchange can be achieved through pipes buried in the sand bar below the water level. However, such measures should be regarded as temporary and viewed with caution because of possible damage to the beach structure or ecology.

## Towed nets or trawls

Towed nets or trawls can be used as booms to recover heavy oil, solid tarballs and debris at sea. Two basic approaches have been developed, which draw upon experience from the fishing industry, see Figures 7.5a and 7.5b. One technique involves a trawl net, which can be towed along the sea surface. The mesh allows the water to escape but retains the oil. It also offers less resistance to water movement than conventional booms, allowing containment at higher speeds. Trawl nets were successfully deployed during the ERIKA and PRESTIGE incidents. Some nets are fitted with detachable cod-ends, which can be replaced once full. The full cod-end can be wrapped in polythene bags and towed away or hoisted onto recovery vessels. A drawback of this system is that considerable amounts of oil tend to adhere to the netting. The difficulty of cleaning contaminated nets is a factor limiting their use and heavily soiled nets often have to be disposed of completely. Extensive logistics, good communication between vessels and skilled and trained responders are also essential.

A similar system can be used to protect sensitive resources, such as estuaries or oyster beds. The net is fixed in position by stakes and uses the force of tidal currents to collect heavy oil and debris. The currents at high tide carry the waste to the filtering cod-end, which automatically closes when the tide goes out, thereby retaining the oil until the next tide comes in and collection begins again.

■ **Barrier constructed from oyster shells, held in place by stakes and nets**

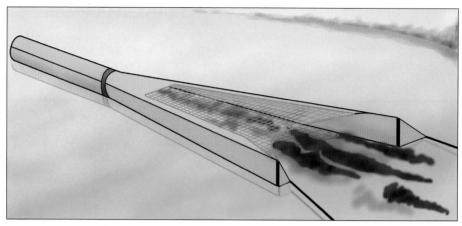

■ **Figure 7.5a: Oil trawl for collecting floating solid oil into a detachable cod-end**

■ **Figure 7.5b: Two vessels corralling floating oil using a purse seine net**

The second approach is based on the purse seine method of fishing. A vertical barrier of netting, towed by boats and supported at regular intervals by poles with floats and weights attached to keep the netting upright, is used to corral and contain oil ready for recovery. The handling and recovery of net boom can, however, be a messy, difficult and time consuming operation.

**Sorbent booms**

These usually consist of a tube of netting or some other fabric filled with a synthetic or natural sorbent material. Booms constructed of sorbent material have little inherent strength and, in some applications, may require additional support. Some also need extra flotation to prevent them from sinking when they become saturated with oil and water. They are normally only used in areas of low current velocity to collect thin films of oil as their recovery efficiency decreases rapidly once the outer layers of the sorbent material become saturated. The handling and disposal of oil soaked sorbent booms can also cause considerable problems.

## 7.2  Recovery

Rapid recovery of contained oil is vital to prevent its escape and the contamination of other areas. Recovery can be achieved using skimmers, pumps, sorbents, manual techniques and non-specialised mechanical equipment, such as vacuum trucks.

### 7.2.1  Skimmer Mechanisms and Design

A skimmer is a device designed to recover oil or oil/water mixtures from the surface of water. Skimmers may be operated from vessels, used from shore or self-propelled. Though their design varies considerably, all skimmers incorporate an element to allow for the recovery of oil in preference to water and some form of flotation or support arrangement. In addition, a pump or vacuum device is necessary to transfer recovered oil and water to storage. More complicated designs can have several recovery elements, integral storage tanks or oil/water separation facilities.

The mechanisms through which oil is removed from the water surface include oleophilic ('oil loving') systems relying on adhesion of oil to a moving surface, suction systems, weir systems relying on gravity and systems that physically lift the oil with mechanical scoops, belts or grabs.

**Oleophilic skimmers**

These skimmers comprise an oleophilic surface to which oil readily adheres, but water does not. Oleophilic materials are usually made from some form of polymer, although metal surfaces have also been shown to be effective. The olephilic parts can be in the form of a disc, belt, brush, rope mop or drum that rotates, lifting the oil from the water surface. Once clear of the water the oil is scraped or squeezed off the oleophilic material and allowed to drop into a sump from where it is pumped to storage. These types of skimmers often recover a high ratio of oil in relation to water (known as the recovery efficiency) and work best with medium viscosity oils. Low viscosity oils such as diesel or kerosene do not accumulate on the oleophilic surfaces in sufficiently thick layers for high recovery rates to be attained. Higher viscosity oils such as heavy bunker oil are excessively sticky and can prove difficult to remove, clogging up moving parts, while viscous water-in-oil emulsions can be almost non-adhesive.

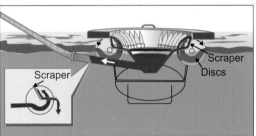

▪ Small oleophilic disc skimmer; oil adheres to the rotating discs to be scraped off into a sump for pumping to storage. Requires a suitable pump and hydraulic power supply

▪ Rope mop skimmer; interwoven sorbent loops form a continuous mop to which oil adheres. Powered rollers squeeze the oil into a storage tank

## Suction skimmers
These are non-oleophilic skimmers. The simplest design is a suction device, where oil is recovered by pumps or air suction systems directly from the water surface. Examples include vacuum trucks or trailers that combine the elements of recovery, storage, transport and oil/water separation. They are often readily available locally to a spill site, either commercially or from municipal or agricultural sources. Provided there is suitable access, these can be positioned on beaches or at quaysides. Vacuum systems are particularly suitable for the recovery of gas/diesel oils, fresh crude oils, most crude oil emulsion and medium fuel oils. The recovery rate is lower for high viscosity oils and emulsions or when pumping over long distances. Where regulations allow, water collected with the oil can be periodically drained off from the bottom of the tank to maximise the storage capacity. For remote areas or beaches that are too soft for vehicles, hand-held vacuum systems are available.

▪ Vacuum trucks are ideally suited to recover oil on or near the shoreline

▪ Portable vacuum systems can be used to recover oil on sand beaches and rocky shorelines. The compact system allows work in areas that may be difficult to reach, although storage is limited

## Weir skimmers
Greater selection of oil may be achieved with the attachment of a weir to the suction hose. Weir skimmers use gravity to selectively drain oil from the surface of the water. By positioning the lip of the weir at or just slightly below the interface between the floating oil and water, the oil flows over the weir to be selectively recovered with minimal amounts of water. Weir skimmers can be very simple rudimentary devices, see Figure 7.6, or more advanced with adjustable weirs and self-levelling arrangements to maintain accurate vertical positioning. No weir skimmer is effective in

steep waves, although swell alone does not usually interfere with skimmer operations. To overcome friction losses along transfer hoses, some weir skimmers have an onboard pump so that the recovered oil is pushed along the hose rather than relying on suction.

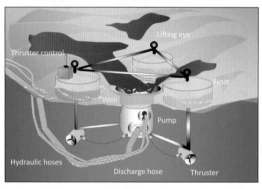

■ A weir skimmer; typically oil flows over the weir into a collection point where it is pumped to storage

■ Figure 7.6: Improvised weir skimmer constructed from plastic bottles and metal offcuts, attached to a vacuum pump

## Other skimmer types

Some skimmer types have been adapted to cope better with waves and rougher seas. Upward rotating belts, for instance, can be partially lowered beneath the oil/water interface to reduce the influence of surface waves. The oil is then scraped

off the belt as it rises above the surface and drops into a storage tank or other containers. Belts may be constructed from oleophilic material, as previously described, relying on the adhesion of the oil to individual elements of a rotating brush, chain link or mesh. Others use buckets or paddles on the belt to aid lifting of the oil from the water surface. Some belt designs may incorporate a combination of such features. Downward rotating belts push the oil down into the water and then capture it when it re-surfaces within a quiescent collection area behind the belt.

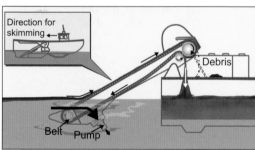

■ A belt skimmer; the belt constructed from a mesh allows water to drain through and encourages adhesion of the oil. The oil is lifted on-board the recovery vessel and is scraped off to storage

The localised water currents induced by rotating discs, belts and drums may be sufficient to allow oils of light to moderate viscosity to flow naturally towards a skimmer once recovery commences. Designs utilising toothed discs or belts to 'grab' the oil may enhance flow of more viscous oils and draw the oil into the skimmer. The high viscosity of some oils or emulsions can eventually prevent flow towards the device and continued recovery will be possible only if some form of propulsion is provided to allow the skimmer to move to the oil or if the oil is pushed towards the skimmer.

Several skimmer systems have been designed for operation in fast flowing waters or at higher towing speeds. The approach typically followed is to increase the area behind the collecting aperture, causing the velocity of the water and oil to slow upon entry to the skimmer and the oil to surface for collection. To be effective, such systems must be able to cope with large volumes of fast flowing water and overcome the turbulence created.

| | Skimmer | Recovery Rate | Oils | Sea State | Debris | Ancillaries |
|---|---|---|---|---|---|---|
| **Oleophilic** | Disc | Dependent on number and size of discs. Tests show grooved discs can be highly effective. | Most effective in medium viscosity oils. | In low waves and current, can be highly selective with little entrained water. However, can be swamped in choppy waters. | Can be clogged by debris. | Separate power pack, hydraulic and discharge hoses, pump, and suitable storage required. |
| | Rope mop | Dependent on number and velocity of ropes. Generally low recovery rate. | Most effective in medium oils although can be effective in heavy oil. | Very little, or no, entrained water. Can operate in choppy waters. | Able to tolerate significant debris, ice and other obstructions. | Small units have built-in power supply and storage. Larger units require separate ancillaries. |
| | Drum | Dependent on number and size of drums. Tests show grooved drums are more effective. | Most effective in medium viscosity oils. | In low waves and current, can be highly selective with little entrained water. However, can be swamped in choppy waters. | Can be clogged by debris. | Separate power pack, hydraulic and discharge hoses, pump and suitable storage required. |
| | Brush | Throughput dependent on number and velocity of brushes. Generally mid-range recovery rate. | Different brush sizes for light, medium and heavy oils. | Very little, or no, entrained water. Some designs can operate in choppy waters, others would be swamped in waves. | Effective in small debris but can be clogged by large debris. | Separate power pack, hydraulic and discharge hoses, pump, storage. |
| | Belt | Low to mid-range recovery rate. | Most effective in medium to heavy oils. | Can be highly selective with little entrained water. Can operate in choppy waters. | Effective in small debris but can be clogged by large debris. | Can deliver oil directly to storage at the top of the belt. Ancillaries required to discharge from a vessel to shore. |
| **Non-olephilic** | Vacuum/ suction | Dependent upon vacuum pump. Generally low to mid-range recovery rate. | Most effective in light to medium oils. | Used in calm waters. Choppy waters will result in collection of excessive water. Addition of a weir can be more selective. | Can be clogged by debris. | Vacuum trucks and trailers are generally self-contained with necessary power supply, pump and storage. |
| | Weir | Dependent upon pump capacity, oil type etc. Recovery rate can be significant. | Effective in light to heavy oils. Very heavy oils may not flow to the weir. | Can be highly selective in calm water with little entrained oil. Can be easily swamped with increase in entrained water. | Can be clogged by debris although some pumps can cope with small debris. | Separate power pack, hydraulic and discharge hoses, pump and storage. Some skimmers have built-in pumps. |
| | Belt | Low to mid-range recovery rate. | Most effective in heavy oils. | Can be highly selective with little entrained water. Can operate in choppy waters. | Effective in small debris. Clogged by large debris. | As for oleophilic belt skimmer. |
| | Drum | Mid-range recovery rate. | Effective with heavy oils. | Can be highly selective in calm water with little entrained oil. However can be swamped in waves. | As for weir skimmer. | As for weir skimmer. |

■ Table 7.4: Generic characteristics of commonly encountered skimmer types

## 7.2.2 Selection of Skimmers

Many factors should be considered when selecting skimmers. The intended use and expected operational conditions should be identified before criteria such as size, robustness and ease of operation, handling and maintenance. The most important considerations are the viscosity and adhesive properties of the spilt oil, including any change in these properties over time. In predictable situations, such as oil terminals and refineries, the type of oil handled is usually known and a more specialised skimmer can be selected, otherwise it is preferable to retain versatility and select units that can deal with a range of oils. Some skimmer designs incorporate interchangeable heads to allow the skimmer to be used with oils of varying viscosities.

■ A weir skimmer in action

■ A recovery system comprising booms, skimmers and reception barges. Due to the semi-solid nature of the oil, the skimmers are essentially operating as mechanical grabs deployed from crane barges

 It is important to have adequate temporary oil storage facilities available, otherwise this becomes a bottleneck to successful oil recovery.

### 7.2.3    Operating Practices

Only in specific situations is it possible to use a skimmer effectively without the aid of a boom to concentrate and retain floating oil. Deployment strategies for booms will, therefore, largely determine the operating practices for skimmers. At sea, towed systems involve skimmers deployed from vessels. Moored boom systems are used in nearshore shallow water and skimmers are usually deployed from land.

The application of dispersants in tandem with skimming operations is to be strongly discouraged since the underlying principles of the two methods are mutually exclusive and oil dispersed into the water column cannot be recovered using surface skimmers. Furthermore, dispersants change the surface properties of the oil and, when applied in proximity to oleophilic skimmers in particular, can render such devices ineffective.

**Recovery at Sea**
To concentrate floating oil at sea, booms can be towed in 'U', 'V' or 'J' configurations using two vessels, as discussed in Section 7.1.6. The recovery device is either deployed as part of the boom array or is deployed separately from a third vessel behind the boom. In both cases the problems of coordinating a multi-ship system are considerable. The skimmer should be kept in the maximum thickness of oil, yet the boom must be protected from abrasion and other mechanical damage. Wave reflection against large skimmers can interfere with the oil flow to the recovery element. In situations involving large slicks of freshly spilt oil that remains coherent, homogenous and thick, recovery may be achieved without containment if spreading is limited.

Skilful handling of the equipment is called for, with continuous adjustments as conditions change. Ideally, the vessel used as a working platform should have lifting gear on deck and manoeuvrability sufficient to quickly assume the desired orientation and maintain it against winds and currents. The rate of oil concentration by towed booms can be slow and a single skimmer may be sufficient to serve several boom arrays.

Temporary storage units need to be easy to handle and easy to empty once full so that they can be used repeatedly. Suitable units include barges and portable tanks, which can be set up on vessels of opportunity. When recovering very viscous oils, storage tanks may need to be heated to allow them to be emptied.

Because of the difficulties of operating multi-ship systems, oil concentration, recovery and storage functions can be combined in a single ship system using a flexible or rigid sweeping arm arrangement.

Flexible systems employ a boom attached to an outrigger. However, if the swath is too wide, the setup can become prone to damage in rough weather or large swell and manoeuvrability can be restricted, severely affecting vessel handling. In such systems, the skimmer is positioned at the apex of the boom where oil is highly concentrated. The skimmer may be free floating or built into the side of a vessel that has a suitable opening to allow the ingress of oil.

Rigid systems comprise a solid floating barrier or sweeping arm deployed from a vessel by crane or hydraulic arms. The skimmer, usually a weir or brush depending on the oil to be recovered, is

■ A single ship system in heavily emulsified crude oil comprising curtain boom attached to an outrigger

built into the arm, close to the vessel to facilitate recovery. The comparative ease of deployment and straightforward design are strong factors contributing to the success of rigid sweeping systems.

Flexible or rigid systems can be used from specially designed vessels or from vessels of opportunity with suitable fittings. Dredgers, coastal tankers and bunker barges have been shown to be effective for the recovery of large volumes of floating oil as their storage capacities allow for longer periods at sea before discharge is required. Handling of recovered oil will be assisted by the high-capacity pumps with which such vessels are typically equipped and the fact that storage tanks are often fitted with heating coils.

■ **A dredger adapted for oil spill recovery operations, incorporating two sweeping arm skimmers. Each arm comprises a steel barrier supported by a lattice frame and floats with a weir and integral pump at the apex of the arm and vessel hull. Forward motion of the vessel imparts a flow over the weir**

### VOLGONEFT 263 – Sweden, 1990

In May 1990 the tanker VOLGONEFT 263 was in collision with a general cargo vessel in dense fog about 15 miles off the Swedish east cost, near Karlskrona. The tanker was carrying a full cargo of waste oil, comprising a mixture of residual fuel oils, diesel and lube oils, of which approximately 840 tonnes was spilt from two damaged tanks.

Immediately after the collision the crew of the VOLGONEFT 263 attempted to prevent the spread of oil by deploying a boom carried on board for such emergencies. In the event, the outflow of oil quickly swamped the boom. However, the Swedish Coast Guard was able to deploy additional booms and start oil recovery operations within a few hours of the collision. Further units were brought in from other regions during the course of the first day.

Weather conditions were exceptionally calm and ideal for recovery operations as the spilt oil neither spread nor drifted as quickly as would otherwise be expected. To take advantage of this opportunity the Swedish Coast Guard requested assistance from neighbouring countries under the provisions of the Helsinki Convention. In response, Denmark, Germany, Finland and the USSR contributed one oil combating vessel each. A Swedish Coast Guard liaison officer was posted on each vessel to ensure that good communications were maintained throughout the fleet.

A total of 9 oil recovery vessels and approximately 15 support craft were involved in a variety of tasks including reconnaissance, boom towing, oil recovery and oil transfer. Two Coast Guard reconnaissance aircraft fitted with remote sensing instrumentation were available for the purpose of locating floating oil day and night. A helicopter was also used for directing skimming operations. After six days working, it was estimated that a total of 900 cubic metres of oil/water mixture had been collected. Most of the remaining oil dispersed naturally at sea and only minor quantities came ashore. The emergency response operation was stood down two weeks after the spill. The response to the VOLGONEFT 263 represented a very successful at-sea recovery operation and the large amounts of oil recovered limited the shoreline impact. The incident benefitted from calm weather, cold water and an organised team of international responders who tested their contingency plans together on an annual basis.

## Recovery Nearshore

Self propelled skimmers can be used to good effect in the calmer waters of ports and harbours, where they may also serve some secondary function such as debris collection. These vessels are often an integral part of response arrangements for oil terminals and refineries, where the pollution risk is relatively well known and a planned response is straightforward. Self propelled skimmers are comparatively expensive but have a known performance and work best in confined areas, particularly where access from the shore is impractical. However, clean-up work should be suspended if there is a risk of fire and explosion because of confinement.

■ **Self propelled weir skimmer recovering oil at a sheltered rocky inlet. The shallow draught of the vessel allows work close to shore. Operators assist by moving oil close to the mouth of the weir**

Wind and water movement will cause oil to accumulate along the shore, which can be concentrated further with the aid of booms. As debris will collect in the same places, skimmers must be capable of operating in the presence of debris. Oleophilic rope mop skimmers, which are less constrained by debris than other types, may be most effective. It may be necessary to work from shallow draught vessels, but it is usually easier to operate skimmers from the shore, particularly if road access, hard standing or a flat working area is available close to the oil collection point.

Skimmers can also be operated from cranes on dock walls and jetties or, if the oil is sufficiently thick, some types of pump can be placed directly into the oil. Once the best site has been identified for skimming operations, careful thought must be given to providing logistical support.

### Recovery in Ice

The recovery of oil in ice presents a number of specific problems not least that oil may be trapped within the ice itself. Devices to crush the oil, allowing recovery, are the subject of ongoing research. A fundamental problem with this approach, however, is that typically the concentration of oil in the recovered oily ice is very low and in such instances better recovery rates may be achieved following a period of thaw.

© Lamor

■ **A brush skimmer designed for operation in extreme cold and broken ice conditions**

Most skimmers operate at a reduced efficiency in ice. Brush belt skimmers, assisted by steam heating jets that enhance the separation of oil from ice, have been shown to be one of the more effective techniques in these conditions. The use of rope mop skimmers may allow free floating oil to be recovered between drift ice, although the machinery runs the risk of seizing up in the cold. Oil recovery may also be achieved using response vessels equipped with sweeping arms to contain the oil, while mechanical grabs transfer the oil and ice into containers on the vessels' decks. Research is being undertaken to define the limitations of existing technologies and to find ways of adapting equipment to improve oil recovery in ice covered waters.

### 7.2.4    Performance/Limitations of Skimmers

 **Even moderate wave action can markedly reduce the effectiveness of most skimmer designs and in the open sea their operation may be severely restricted.**

The performance of skimmers is improved in sheltered waters and in thick layers of oil provided that the type, viscosity and thickness of the oil spilt is within the capabilities of the skimmer in question.

In open seas, small skimming units are easily swamped, while larger skimmers possess greater inertia and are unable to follow the wave profiles. In currents exceeding about 0.5 ms$^{-1}$ (1 knot), the performance of skimmers may be impaired due to the tendency for floating oil to escape confinement by booms. This limitation is partly overcome in self-propelled skimmers, where an oleophilic mop array or belt is rotated so that its velocity relative to the floating oil is effectively reduced when the vessel is underway.

The viscosity of the oils to be recovered also has a considerable effect on the performance of skimmers. Oils with high pour points, such as heavy crude and fuel oils, generally do not flow easily. If the ambient temperature is below the pour point, the oil will effectively behave as a solid and will not flow towards the skimmer readily. Some skimmers have integrated screw pumps that mechanically push the oil, making them more tolerant to highly viscous, solidified oils and debris, but the internal resistances of hoses and pipes may still be an issue.

The application of steam heating may be helpful to reduce blocking of pumps and hoses. Where viscosity increases are due to the formation of water-in-oil emulsions, chemical emulsion breakers can be employed providing they are mixed in well. It may also be appropriate to swap the type of skimmer being used. For example, systems such as oleophilic skimmers may be able to operate efficiently in fresh oil found early in an incident. However, with the increases in viscosity and possible inclusion of debris, recovery may become more effective with weir skimmers using screw pumps with debris cutters.

The pumping phase of the skimming process is another factor determining the overall performance of a device because all pumps lose efficiency, albeit at different rates, as oil viscosity increases over time.

It is also important to recognise the difficulties posed by floating debris, both natural (seaweeds, seagrasses, trees and branches) and manmade (plastic, glass, timber). Skimmers may need trash screens and regular unblocking in places where debris is common, such as near urban areas or river mouths.

Hoses carrying oil from the skimmer should be fitted with the correct flotation to prevent them interfering with the behaviour of the skimmer. All hoses can be troublesome to handle when oily and should be fitted with effective but simple couplings. A selection of adapters can be useful for matching hoses of different diameters and for joining incompatible connectors.

 **Because of the various constraints imposed on skimmers in the field, it is rarely possible to achieve their theoretical design capacities during an actual spill.**

### 7.2.5 Maintenance

All skimmers require supervision to ensure that oil is reaching the collection element and debris is not accumulating and reducing efficiency or causing damage. Although they are generally robust, skimmers and related equipment may break down through damage, incorrect use, age, etc. Repair will usually require specialised knowledge and access to replacement parts. The use of suitably trained operational personnel, with an understanding of equipment limitation and the ability to strip down the machine and to rebuild as required, will reduce unwarranted delays.

After use, skimmers should be cleaned and overhauled to identify and rectify any wear and damage. Steam lances or solvents can be used to remove oil but cleaning chemicals should not be used on sorbent mops and plastic discs. Skimmers and their power packs should be protected from damage, damp and corrosion from salt atmospheres. Sorbent mops, rubber belts and plastic materials incorporated in skimmers will perish if exposed to direct sunlight for long periods. Regular inspections and testing of equipment is essential, particularly as its use may be infrequent.

### PRESTIGE – Spain, 2002

During severe weather on 13th November 2002, the tanker PRESTIGE, carrying a cargo of 77,000 tonnes of heavy fuel oil, began listing and leaking oil while 30 nautical miles off Cabo Fisterra (Galicia, Spain). The vessel finally broke in two on 19th November, releasing a significant amount of oil, and sank some 140 nautical miles west of Vigo (Spain). Oil continued to leak from the wreck at a slowly declining rate. In total, some 63,000 tonnes of oil were estimated to have been spilt.

The amount and persistent nature of the oil, together with the prevailing currents, indicated that significant quantities of oil would remain at sea for some time and a major offshore clean-up operation was launched, involving a fleet of specialised vessels from Spain and nine other European countries. Over a thousand fishing vessels also participated in the clean-up. Although the specialised vessels recovered a significant volume of oil, local fishermen recovered double this amount using non-specialised boats and gear. The low freeboard of the fishing vessels allowed manual collection of oil by long handled scoops and mechanically by the use of nets and trawls and by grabs attached to vessel cranes. The success of the fishing vessels was a result of their sheer numbers, their ability to manoeuvre very close to the shore to recover oil, and the fact that they could recover plates of oil too small and too spread out the for the larger specialised vessels.

The combined at-sea recovery operation off Spain reportedly removed almost 50,000 tonnes of oil-water mixture. However this, and the extensive booming of estuaries and sensitive areas, failed to prevent shoreline contamination, which extended from the northern Portuguese border along the entire northern coast of Spain and along the west and north coasts of France.

■ **Local fishermen mobilised in significant numbers to assist with oil collection following the PRESTIGE spill**

### 7.2.6 Other Recovery Methods

Items of non specialist equipment can be used to supplement skimming operations or to provide a suitable alternative when skimmers are unavailable or ineffective.

## Mechanical grabs

As viscous and semi-solid lumps of oil can cause problems for a wide variety of skimmers, a more effective and cheaper method of recovery for these type of oils is to scoop the oil from the water using crane mounted clamshell buckets or other mechanical grabs operated from shore or on a suitable vessel, such as a dredger. Oil dredgers can collect half a tonne of oil at a time when placed in thick accumulations of oil. Another advantage is that they can usually deliver the oil directly into the hold of a recovery vessel or into a temporary storage barge. The mechanical grab approach has been used successfully in a number of spills.

## Manual recovery

In the absence of mechanical grabs, simple hand-held equipment, such as buckets, rakes and shovels, can be used to scoop up the oil or oily debris. Nets are also useful collection devices, particularly for thicker lumps of oil and oily seaweed or other oiled material.

■ **The use of mechanical grabs is an effective means of recovery for semi-solid lumps of oil**

In many major spills, fishing vessels have been deployed to assist in the manual recovery efforts.

■ **Semi-solid oil removed from the sea surface using scoops**

## Sorbents

Oil sorbents comprise a wide range of products that soak up oil in preference to water. They act either by adsorption or absorption. Adsorption occurs when the liquid recovered (i.e. the oil) is distributed over the surface of the product. Absorption occurs when the liquid is incorporated into the body or pores of the material, causing it to swell. With absorbents the oil combines with the material in such a way that it will not leak out nor can it be squeezed out. The majority of sorbents available are classed as adsorbents. There are three main kinds of sorbents:

- Natural organic materials, such as bark, peat moss, straw, hay, feathers, coconut husks, sugar cane waste (bagasse)
- inorganic materials, such as vermiculite, perlite and volcanic ash
- synthetic organic sorbents, such as polyurethane foam and polypropylene fibres.

Synthetic organic sorbents usually have the greatest capacity for oil retention relative to their own volume and can be obtained in a variety of forms, including fibres, mops, sheets and pillows. They are reusable to some extent.

Some sorbents, particularly natural ones, can be treated with oleophilic agents or by controlled heating, which improves the ability of the material to be preferentially wetted by oil rather than water. This improves their performance and prevents them from becoming waterlogged and sinking.

The use of sorbents is usually only appropriate during the final stages of clean-up or to help remove thin films of oil from inaccessible locations. It is not advocated as a primary response tool to a major spill at sea. Application is normally by hand or, in the case of large scale use of loose material, using a blower.

In sensitive areas, such as marshes, natural sorbents may sometimes be useful to immobilise the oil and minimise the contamination of vegetation and birds. In such situations it may be appropriate to leave the oil-soaked sorbent to degrade naturally unless it is likely to migrate and contaminate other areas.

It is, however, usually necessary to recover all the oil soaked material so that the presence of sorbents does not exacerbate problems caused by the oil. This is normally done manually or using belt skimmers; other skimmers can become clogged by sorbent materials.

## Solidifiers or gelling agents

Although not an oil recovery technique in its own right, chemicals have been developed that convert liquid oil into solid or 'rubbery' mats, like buoyant gel, thereby facilitating recovery by manual means or nets. The use of such chemicals has been tested successfully in the laboratory, but the difficulties of applying and mixing the chemicals into the oil, the high cost and the large amount of chemical required are likely to preclude their use, except for small pockets of oil in restricted locations such as harbours.

# 7.3 Success of At-Sea Operations

 **The success of an at-sea operation is not directly related to the quantity or percentage of oil recovered, but is judged best by how much it reduces the extent of affected shoreline.**

An at-sea operation that reduces the length of the contaminated beach from, say, 10 km to 5 km is more successful than one that reduces the average level of oiling from a 2 cm to a 1 cm thick layer of oil along 10 km of beach. For example, the response to the BALTIC CARRIER a double hulled chemical tanker that suffered a collision off the coast of

Germany in 2001, was deemed a success because it captured 400 tonnes of oil that had drifted in the current beyond the affected shoreline areas, thereby avoiding the oiling of additional coastline.

The major difficulty with at-sea recovery is not being able to encounter enough oil to contain and remove meaningful quantities. Liquid oil begins to spread the moment it hits the water, yet even if response vessels are mobilised quickly they generally need hours, if not days, to arrive on site. Therefore, the encounter rate is invariably low. By the time skimming operations can begin, oil is often fragmented over many square kilometres of open sea, has moved beyond the reach of response vessels into shallow or rocky coastal waters, or has already stranded on the shoreline. This is the main reason why containment and recovery operations at sea rarely result in the removal of more than a relatively small proportion of oil spilt, usually only 10 - 15% and often considerably less. Nevertheless, there are occasions when the release is not sudden and there is sufficient warning for emergency response vessels to mobilise and arrive on site. In such situations, and with calm seas and adequate logistical support, properly equipped response vessels can potentially contain and recover a larger percentage of oil.

---

**ERIKA – France, 1999**

Following the spill of 20,000 tonnes of heavy fuel oil from the tanker ERIKA in December 1999, the French Naval Command in Brest took charge of operations at sea in accordance with the National Contingency Plan. Since the oil was not amenable to chemical dispersion, the French Navy mobilised a number of vessels for offshore oil recovery. The governments of Germany, the Netherlands, Spain and the United Kingdom also provided vessels to assist the response under the terms of the Bonn Agreement, a cooperative arrangement for combating marine pollution between North Sea countries. The first recovery vessel arrived on site the day after the incident, but storm conditions and wave heights exceeding 6 metres made deployment of any equipment hazardous. Recovery efforts resumed 2 days later, but attempts at skimming ultimately met with little success owing to the generally poor weather, the widespread fragmentation of the slick and the viscous and sticky nature of the water-in-oil emulsion which made pumping difficult. Poor weather also caused the rupture of high seas containment booms. In 15 days of operations 1,100 tonnes of oil/water mixture were collected, mainly during a 24 hour period of relatively calm weather and reduced swell. This represented less than 3% the total spill volume and oiling subsequently occurred over some 400 km of shoreline, requiring a major shoreline clean-up operation.

# THE USE OF DISPERSANTS

When used appropriately, dispersants can be an effective response to an oil spill. They are capable of rapidly removing large amounts of certain types of oil from the sea surface and transferring them to the water column. Following dispersant application, wave energy will cause the oil slick to break up into small oil droplets that are rapidly diluted and subsequently biodegraded by microorganisms occurring naturally in the marine environment. They can also delay the formation of persistent water-in-oil emulsions. In common with other response techniques, the decision to use dispersants must be given careful consideration and take into account oil characteristics, sea and weather conditions, environmental sensitivities and national regulations on dispersant use. Significant environmental and economic benefits can be achieved, particularly when other at-sea response techniques are limited by weather conditions or the availability of resources.

 In certain situations dispersants may be the only way to quickly remove significant quantities of surface oil, thereby minimising or preventing damage to important sensitive resources.

## 8.1 Mechanism of Dispersion and Dispersant Composition

Following a spill, some of the oil will disperse naturally into the water column. The extent to which this occurs depends on the type of oil spilt and the mixing energy of the sea. Oils with a lower viscosity are more amenable to natural dispersion than ones with a higher viscosity. Natural dispersion takes place when the mixing energy provided by the waves and wind is sufficient to overcome surface tension at the oil/water interface and break the oil slick into droplets of variable sizes. Generally, larger oil droplets will rapidly resurface and then coalesce to form an oil slick, but the smaller droplets will remain suspended in the water column due to wave motion and turbulence and will be further diluted by subsurface currents.

The process of natural dispersion takes place in moderately rough seas with breaking waves and winds above 5 ms$^{-1}$ (10 knots). By way of example, severe storm conditions in Shetland, UK, at the time of the grounding of the MT BRAER, caused almost all of the 84,000 tonne cargo of Gulfaks North Sea crude oil, a very low viscosity oil, to be dispersed naturally and with minimal shoreline impact, see Figure 8.2.

Dispersants are designed to enhance natural dispersion by reducing the surface tension at the oil/water interface, making it easier for waves to create small oil droplets.

Dispersants are a blend of surfactants (surface active agents) in a solvent. The solvent has two functions:

- Reducing the viscosity of the surfactant so that it can be sprayed

- promoting penetration of the surfactant into the oil slick.

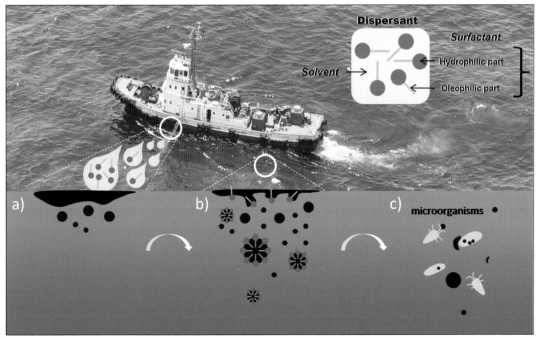

■ **Figure 8.1: The chemical dispersion process.** **a)** Dispersant containing surfactants and solvent is sprayed onto the oil with the solvent carrying the surfactant into the oil. **b)** The surfactant molecules migrate to the oil/water interface and reduce surface tension, allowing small oil droplets to break away from the slick. **c)** The droplets disperse by turbulent mixing and are ultimately degraded by naturally occurring bacteria, fungi, algae etc. This latter stage may require days or weeks to achieve

■ **Figure 8.2: Natural dispersion of spilt oil during the MT BRAER grounding, Shetland, UK, 1993**

The surfactant molecules are the key component of the dispersant. They are made up of two parts: an oleophilic part (oil-loving) and a hydrophilic part (water-loving). When dispersants are sprayed onto an oil slick, the solvent transports and distributes the surfactants through the oil slick to the oil/water interface, where they rearrange so that the oleophilic part of the molecule is in the oil and the hydrophilic part is in the water. This creates a sharp reduction in the surface tension of the oil/water interface and small oil droplets break away from the oil slick with the help of wave energy. Re-coalescence is minimised by the presence of the surfactant molecules on the droplet surface, which act to repel other droplets, and the reduced probability of encountering other oil droplets as they move apart.

 It is important to remember that dispersants remove oil from the water's surface but do not in themselves cause the oil to sink to the bottom.

To achieve an efficient dispersion, oil droplet size must be in the range of 1 μm* to 70 μm, with the most stable size being less than 45 μm. Smaller droplets are better as they remain suspended in the water column, where they are rapidly diluted to below harmful concentrations in the top few metres of the sea. The increased surface area provided by the small droplets also enhances the opportunity for biodegradation of the oil. Biodegradation occurs at the droplet surface, with the degrading organisms using the oil as a food source.

**Types of dispersants**
Dispersants are classed according to their generation and their type. The first generation of products, introduced in the 1960s, were similar to industrial cleaners and degreasers and had high aquatic toxicity. They are no longer used in oil spill response.

Second generation dispersants, also called Type I dispersants, were designed specifically to treat oil spills at sea by spraying from vessels. They contain a hydrocarbon solvent with a low or no aromatic content and typically 15 to 25% surfactant. They are intended to be applied undiluted (neat), as pre-dilution with sea water renders them ineffective. They also require a high dose rate of between 1:1 and 1:3 (dispersant to oil). While having lower

toxicity than the first generation dispersants, they are less effective and may be more toxic than third generation dispersants. In many countries, Type I dispersants are no longer used.

Third generation dispersants contain a blend of two or three surfactants with glycol and light petroleum distillate solvents. The most common surfactants used are non-ionic (fatty acid esters and ethoxylated fatty acid esters) and anionic (sodium alkyl sulphosuccinate). The concentration of surfactant within the solvent tends to be higher than with Type I products, at between 25% and 65%.

Third generation dispersants can be divided into Type II and Type III. Type II dispersants are generally diluted with sea water prior to use, typically at 10% dispersant, but require a high dosage of 2:1 to 1:5 (dispersant/water mix to oil) to be effective. This requirement for dilution limits their use to application from vessels. Type III dispersants are used neat and were primarily developed to allow efficient application from aircraft, but they may also be used from vessels. Dosage rates range between 1:5 and 1:50 (neat dispersant to oil), with the ideal practical ratio determined case by case. Third generation Type III dispersants are now the most commonly available dispersants.

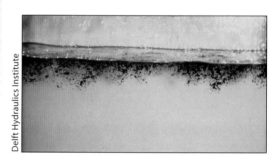
Delft Hydraulics Institute

■ **Oil without dispersant (natural dispersion)**

Delft Hydraulics Institute

■ **Oil with dispersant**

Delft Hydraulics Institute

■ **Oil with dispersant a few seconds later, demonstrating rapid dilution**

* μm = micro-metres (microns) = $10^{-6}$ metres

Dispersants are manufactured primarily for use in the marine environment. Their efficiency will be optimum in waters with a salinity of around 30-35 parts per thousand (ppt). The efficiency of dispersants will decrease rapidly in brackish waters with a salinity below 5-10 ppt, particularly when pre-diluted, and is also affected when salinity rises above 35 ppt. In fresh water, dispersant effectiveness is dramatically reduced because the surfactants tend to travel through the oil layer into the water column instead of stabilising at the oil/water interface. However, some dispersants have been specially formulated for use in fresh water. In a confined fresh water system other factors also need to be considered, such as whether there is sufficient water depth or exchange of water to achieve adequate dilution.

## 8.2 Limitations of Dispersants

 **Dispersant effectiveness is limited by a number of physical and chemical parameters, the most important of which are sea state and oil properties.** An awareness of these limitations is important in order to identify circumstances when dispersant use is appropriate.

### Sea state
A small amount of wave energy is necessary to achieve successful chemical dispersion at sea. In the absence of sufficient wave energy to maintain the dispersion of oil droplets in the water column, they may re-surface and form a slick. However, the efficiency of chemical dispersion will improve with increasing sea state only to a certain level. In severe sea conditions the oil may be submerged by breaking waves, preventing direct contact between the dispersant and the oil. Dispersant sprayed onto water rather than oil will be ineffective. Field trials indicate that a wind speed between 4-12 ms$^{-1}$ (about 8-25 knots) is optimum.

### Oil properties
The properties of the oil and the way these change with time on the sea are important when assessing the likelihood of successful chemical dispersion. The viscosity and pour point of an oil provide a good indication of its dispersability. As a general rule, fresh light to medium crude oils (Group 2 or 3 oils) are considered to be readily dispersible, while highly viscous oils are not. The upper limit of dispersability is likely to be reached with heavier oils (Group 4 oils). Dispersant formulations are continually evolving to improve their effectiveness on heavy fuel oils and other oils with high viscosities. However, as a guide, oils that remain fluid and have a viscosity below 2,000 cSt at the time of the spill are likely to be dispersible, whereas it will become increasingly more difficult to disperse oils with viscosities above this point. Oils with viscosities above 10,000 cSt (assuming the oil is not heated) are highly unlikely to disperse, see Table 8.1. It should be noted that some oils may not be dispersible at viscosities below this value, while others may disperse at higher viscosities depending on the dispersant formulation and the chemical composition of the oil.

Pour point is also an important parameter. Any oil with a pour point higher than the ambient temperature (such oils are usually transported heated) will start to become very viscous as it cools after spillage, and may even become solid. As a general rule, oils with a pour point close to the temperature of the sea will be difficult to disperse.

High viscosity oils, and those with high pour points, do not disperse easily either naturally or after the application of dispersants because the mechanical resistance of the oil prevents small droplets breaking away from under the slick. Furthermore, dispersants are not usually effective for these oils because they are not able to penetrate the oil before being washed off and lost into the surrounding water.

Once an oil has been spilt, the viscosity rapidly increases due to weathering, emulsification and the loss of volatile components through evaporation. Some oils are particularly prone to forming water-in-oil emulsions, which will increase both the viscosity and the volume of the pollutant. However, if the emulsion is unstable, Type III dispersants may be able to break it back to its parent oil, releasing the water and allowing the relatively liquid oil to be dispersed by a second application of dispersant. Because of these changes in oil properties over time, the opportunity for the successful application of dispersants is limited. The time available ('window of opportunity') usually ranges from a few hours to a few days, depending on the type of oil involved and the environmental conditions.

Group 1 oils, such as diesel, gasoline and kerosene, do not readily form emulsions but spread to form very thin films of oil on the water surface (often referred to as 'sheen' because they are iridescent)

© CEDRE

■ **Dispersant droplets 'punching' through the oil and causing a herding effect**

| Crude Name | Loading Port | Country | Gravity °API | Specific gravity | Viscosity cSt 100F 37.8C | Av Pour point C | Av Pour point F |
|---|---|---|---|---|---|---|---|
| Amna (Amal) | Ras Lanuf | Libya | 36 | 0.8 | 13 | 18 | 64 |
| Ardjuna (Arjuna) | Ardjuna | Indonesia | 38 | 0.8 | 3 | 27 | 81 |
| Bachaquero (BCF 17) | La Salina | Venezuela | 16 | 1.0 | 5,000@15C | -29 | -20 |
| **Bahia** | **Salvador** | **Brazil** | **35.2** | **0.8** | **17** | **38** | **100** |
| Bakr | Ras Gharib | Egypt | 20 | 0.9 | 17 | 7 | 45 |
| Bass Strait | | Australia | 46 | 0.8 | 2 | 15 | 59 |
| Beatrice | Nigg Bay | UK | 38 | 0.8 | 7.44 @ 40C | 18 | 64 |
| Belayim | Wadi Feiran | Egypt | 27 | 0.9 | 18 | 6 | 43 |
| Bintulu | Bintulu | Malaysia | 37 | 0.8 | ss | 19 | 66 |
| **Boscan** | **Bajo Grande** | **Venezuela** | **10** | **1.0** | **20000** | **15** | **59** |
| **Bu Attifel** | **Zueitina** | **Libya** | **43** | **0.8** | **-** | **32** | **89.6** |
| Bunju (Bunyu) | Balikpapan | Indonesia | 32 | 0.9 | 3 | 18 | 64 |
| Cabinda (Malongo, Takula) | Malongo Terminal | Angola | 33 | 0.9 | 20 | 12 | 54 |
| Carmopolis | Atalaia | Brazil | 23 | 0.9 | 105 @ 50C | 18 | 64 |
| **Cinta (Cinta Blend, Intan-Cinta)** | **Cinta** | **Indonesia** | **33** | **0.9** | **25 @ 50C** | **43** | **109** |
| Coco | - | Congo | 32 | 0.9 | ss | 21 | 69 |
| Duri (Sumatran Heavy) | Dumai | Indonesia | 21 | 0.9 | 309 @ 40C | 14 | 57 |
| El Morgan (Suez mix) | Ras Shukheir | Egypt | 32 | 0.9 | 9.5 | 7 | 45 |
| **Escravos** | **Escravos** | **Nigeria** | **34** | **0.9** | **9 @ 15C** | **35** | **15** |
| Gamba (Gabon) | SPMB Gamba | Gabon | 31 | 0.9 | 38 | 23 | 73 |
| Gippsland Mix | Long Island Point Terminal | Australia | 50 | 0.8 | 2 | 15 | 59 |
| **Handil** | **Senipah** | **Indonesia** | **33** | **0.9** | **4** | **35** | **95** |
| Heavy Lake Mix | La Salina | Venezuela | 17 | 1.0 | 600 | -12 | 10 |
| Iranian Nowruz (Soroush) | | | 18 | 0.9 | 270 | -26 | -15 |
| **Jatibarang** | **Balongan** | **Indonesia** | **32** | **0.9** | **16.7 @ 50C** | **35** | **95** |
| Jobo | Puerto Ordaz | Venezuela | 12 | 1.0 | 2.8 @ 50C | 30 | 86 |
| Lagunillas | La Salina | Venezuela | 17.7 | 0.9 | 500 | -20 | -5 |
| Mandji | Cape Lopez | Gabon | 30 | 0.9 | 17 | 9 | 48 |
| Merey | Puerto La Cruz | Venezuela | 17 | 1.0 | 520 | -21 | -6 |
| Minas (Sumatran Light, SLC, Sumatran light export blend) | Dumai | Indonesia | 35 | 0.8 | 11.5 @ 50C | 18 | 64 |
| Morichal (Monagas) | Puerto Ordaz | Venezuela | 13.5 | 1.0 | 1350 @ 50C | 0 | 32 |
| **Nile Blend** | **Port Sudan** | **Sudan** | **33** | **0.9** | **ss** | **36** | **97** |
| Norne | Mongstad | Norway | 31 | 0.9 | - | 18 | 64 |
| Panuco | Tampico | Mexico | 13 | 1.0 | 4700 | 2 | 35 |
| Pilon | Carpito | Venezuela | 14 | 1.0 | 1900 | -3 | 27 |
| Qua Iboe | Qua Iboe | Nigeria | 36 | 0.8 | 3.4 | 10 | 50 |
| Quiriquire | Carpito | Venezuela | 16 | 1.0 | 160 | -29 | -20 |
| Ras Lanuf | Ras Lanuf | Libya | 37 | 0.8 | 4 | 7 | 45 |
| Rio Zulia | Santa Marta | Colombia | 41 | 0.8 | 4 | 27 | 80 |
| San Joachim | Puerto La Cruz | Venezuela | 42 | 0.8 | 2 | 24 | 75 |
| Santa Rosa | Puerto La Cruz | Venezuela | 50 | 0.8 | 2 | 10 | 50 |
| Sarir (Sabir/Libyan Export) | Marsa Al Hariga | Libya | 38 | 0.8 | 6.7 @ 50C | 24 | 75 |
| Seria | Seria | Brunei | 36 | 0.8 | 2 | 0-15 | 32-60 |
| Shengli | Tsingtao | China | 24 | 0.9 | 107 @ 50C | 21 | 70 |
| Shiraz | Kharg Island | Iran | 19 | 0.9 | 450 @ 50C | -9 | -23 |
| Statfjord | North Sea | Norway | 40 | 0.8 | 7 @ 10C | 6 | 43 |
| **Taching (Daqing)** | **Dairen** | **China** | **31** | **0.9** | **138** | **35** | **95** |
| Tia Juana Pesada | Puerto Miranda | Venezuela | 12 | 1.0 | 1400 @ 50C | | 30 |
| Wafra Eocene | Mina Saud / Mina Abdulla | neutral zone | 18.6 | 0.9 | 270 | -29 | -20 |
| **Widuri** | **Widuri** | **Indonesia** | **33** | **0.9** | **ss** | **45** | **113** |
| Zaire | Muanda | Zaire | 34 | 0.9 | 20 | 27 | 80 |
| Zeta North | Puerto La Cruz | Venezuela | 35 | 0.8 | 3 | 21 | 70 |

$$°API = \frac{141.5}{\text{Specific Gravity}} - 131.5 \qquad\qquad \text{Specific Gravity} = \frac{141.5}{°API + 131.5}$$

■ **Table 8.1: Crude oils with high viscositites or high pour points**

Oils with high viscosities or pour points will be difficult to disperse, particularly when the sea temperature is significantly colder than the pour point. The crude oils highlighted in bold are highly unlikely to be dispersible in any normal scenario.

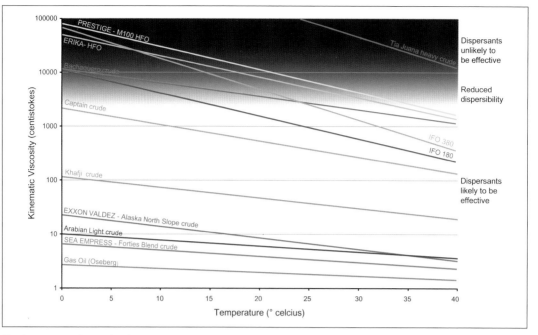

■ **Figure 8.3: Relationship between temperature and oil viscosity for a selection of fresh crude and fuel oils\***

and they readily dissipate without need for the use of dispersants. It is, therefore, not advisable to use dispersants on oils from this group or on sheens that have formed from any crude or fuel oil. This is because the dispersant droplets tend to punch through the thin film or sheen and cause 'herding' of the oil. The dispersant in the water causes the oil film to draw back, creating an immediate area of clear water that should not be mistaken for dispersion.

### Dispersant choice and dosage

Among the factors that influence the amount of oil that can be dispersed are the choice of dispersant and its dosage. Dispersants are manufactured to slightly different formulations and their effectiveness varies with the type of oil treated. Some dispersants have been formulated specifically with the aim of treating viscous oils. Laboratory tests may be carried out to rank one dispersant relative to another for a particular oil and some countries require operators of terminals and rigs to undertake studies to identify the most effective dispersant for the oil involved. However, the results from these tests cannot be extrapolated to predict the amount of oil that will be dispersed at sea as test conditions do not mimic sea conditions. For planning purposes, a dosage of 1:20 dispersant to oil is commonly used and spraying equipment is often pre-configured to achieve this. This dosage may be decreased on fresh oils or increased for viscous or emulsified oils, where more than one application may be needed.

## 8.3 Other Chemical Treating Agents

Degreasers are often carried onboard ships to deal with small spillages of oil on deck, but most are more toxic than dispersant and should not be used as a dispersant at sea or as a shoreline cleaner.

Demulsifiers are agents used to inhibit the formation of water-in-oil emulsions or break down emulsions that have already been created, making subsequent pumping operations easier. There are different types of demulsifiers; some contain polymers that have a low water solubility and may be sprayed directly onto an oil emulsion slick at sea, others contain surfactants that are very soluble in water and best used in closed systems, such as on an emulsion that has been collected following at-sea recovery operations. The aquatic toxicity of these products varies and they are subject to restrictions in a similar way to dispersants. More laboratory and field testing is required before demulsifiers are more commonly used in clean-up operations.

## 8.4 Application Methods

■ **The application of dispersant by boat is best suited to smaller spills near shores**

Dispersants can be applied to oil spilt on open water by boats or aircraft. Large multi-engine

---

\* As a general guide, oils that remain fluid and have a viscosity below 2,000 cSt at the time of the spill are likely to be dispersible, whereas it will become increasingly more difficult to disperse oils with viscosities above this point. The graph does not take account of increases in viscosity due to emulsification.

aircraft are better suited to dealing with major offshore spills while boats, helicopters and light aircraft are often more suitable for treating smaller spills closer to the shore.

The droplet size of the dispersant is important as it needs to be sufficiently large to overcome the effects of wind drift and evaporative loss, but not so large that they 'punch' through the oil slick. The optimum droplet size is between 600 and 800 μm. Ultimately, whichever method of application is used, the key to a successful response using dispersants is the ability to target the thickest part of the oil slick within a short time, before weathering or sea state render the oil undispersable.

### 8.4.1 Vessel Spraying

When dispersants are sprayed from vessels they are usually applied through a set of nozzles mounted on spray arms. Diesel or electric pumps transfer the dispersant from a storage tank through the nozzles, which are calibrated to produce a uniform spray pattern of droplets. Spray units can be portable or permanently installed on a vessel and systems are available to deliver the dispersant either undiluted or diluted with sea water.

Spray arms are usually mounted as far forward on the vessel as possible to avoid the effect of the bow wave, which can push the oil beyond the spray swath. Mounting the spray arms on the bow allows the vessel to travel faster and, because freeboard is often greater at the bow, also allows the spray arms to be made longer. This optimises the amount of oil that can be treated ('encounter rate') with a limited

■ **Dispersant spray system**

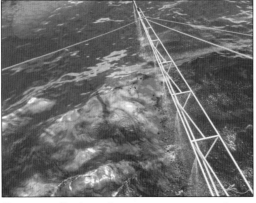

■ **Boat application using spray arms mounted near the bow of the vessel**

dispersant payload. However, if the arms are too long they risk damage when the vessel rolls.

■ **Application of dispersant using fire monitors on a tug, showing uneven spread of dispersant and the effect of wind**

If spray arms are not available, fire hoses or monitors are sometimes used to apply diluted concentrate dispersants, but optimum dilution of the dispersant is difficult to achieve because of the very high flow rates, so wastage is a common problem. The high-powered jet of water also makes it difficult to apply the dispersant as a uniform spray of droplet and it is frequently forced through the oil, making it ineffective. Therefore, fire monitors are unlikely to be an effective application tool unless specially modified for the purpose.

Vessels offer certain advantages for dispersant spraying because they are usually readily available, easy to load and deploy, have cost advantages over aircraft and can apply dispersant fairly accurately to specific areas of a slick. Nevertheless, they also have serious limitations, particularly for larger spills, because of the low treatment rate that they offer and the difficulty of locating the heaviest concentrations of oil from the bridge of a vessel. These problems can be partially overcome by directing the operation from a spotter aircraft.

### 8.4.2 Aerial Spraying

The application of dispersants from aircraft offers the advantages of rapid response, high treatment rates and optimum dispersant use. In broad terms, three types of aircraft are used; those designed for agricultural or pest control operations, which require minor modification for dispersant application, those that have been adapted specifically for the application of dispersant, and cargo aircraft with modular tanks. The first category tend to be single-engined aircraft with small payloads; these can operate from rural airstrips or landing grounds close to the scene of an incident and are often most suitable for small spills or fragmented slicks close to shore. Larger multi-engined aircraft offer the required range, payload and speed for the treatment of large spills far offshore, but they need longer runways and greater operational support, have longer turn-around times and more restricted visibility and manoeuvrability. For safety reasons, some aviation authorities prefer the use of aircraft with at least two engines.

© CEDRE

■ **Fixed wing aircraft fitted with spray boom**

Several types of helicopter have also been adapted to spray dispersants, although most are equipped with a cargo hook for lifting underslung loads and can, therefore, carry a bucket spray system without the need for modification. Spraying is controlled from the cockpit, with an electrical remote control unit attached by cable to the spray system. Helicopters are often readily available, can spray in confined situations, and operate from a base very near to the spill site. Their main disadvantage is their relatively low speed and limited payload and range. However, helicopters can potentially reload dispersants from a vessel or offshore oil platform for operations offshore.

The ideal aircraft will be determined primarily by the size and location of the spill although, in reality, local availability is more likely to be the crucial factor.

Only Type III dispersants are suitable for aerial spraying as they require no mixing beyond that provided by the natural movement of the sea. The relatively low dosage (typically 1:20) also makes the best use of the available payload. Aircraft spraying systems consist of a pump that draws dispersant at a controlled rate from a tank into spray arms fitted on the aircraft. The dispersant is discharged through either pressure nozzles or wind driven rotating units, spaced at regular intervals along the spray arm, which are designed to produce dispersant droplets of the optimum size. Both types of discharge unit can be used on most light aircraft and helicopters, but larger aircraft will use pressure nozzles.

### 8.4.3 Application Rate

To work out the appropriate application rate, the ratio of dispersant to oil required for effective dispersion has to be selected. This can range from 1:1 for Type I dispersants to 1:50 for Type III dispersants, depending on the application method, the type of dispersant, the oil type and the prevailing conditions. The application rate can be calculated in two steps, as follows:

- Estimation of the volume of oil to be treated based on observations and assumptions concerning the average thickness and area of the slick

- calculation of the quantity of dispersant needed to achieve the required dosage (dispersant: oil ratio).

It has been found that although there are substantial variations in the thickness of the oil within a slick, most fresh oils spread within a few hours so that, overall, the average thickness is 0.1 mm ($10^{-4}$ m). This thickness is often used as the basis upon which to plan operations and gives the volume of oil in one hectare (10,000 square metres, $10^4$ m$^2$) as:

$$10^{-4} \text{ m} \times 10^4 \text{ m}^2 = 1 \text{ m}^3 \text{ or } 1,000 \text{ litres}$$

For a dosage of 1:20, the quantity of dispersant required would be:

$$\frac{1000 \text{ litres}}{20} = 50 \text{ litres}$$

The application rate would be

50 litres/hectare (4.5 imp. gal/acre).

Image courtesy of Lehmann/USCG

■ **Application of dispersant to the spill from the DEEPWATER HORIZON well blowout, offshore Louisiana, USA**

The discharge rate can be calculated by multiplying the application rate (litre/m²) by the swath width of the spraying arm (m) and the speed of the aircraft or vessel (ms⁻¹).

As an example, if dispersants were applied by an aircraft travelling at a speed of 45 ms⁻¹ (90 knots) with a swath width of 15 m and an application rate of 50 litres/hectare (0.005 litre/m²), the discharge rate would be:

Discharge rate = 0.005 litres/m² × 15 m × 45 ms⁻¹
= 3.37 litres/s (or about 200 litres/minute).

Therefore, to disperse a slick of 0.1 mm thickness at a dose rate of 1:20, the discharge rate of the pump of the spraying system would need to be adjusted to a rate of about 200 litres per minute. The same calculation is made to determine the discharge rate for vessel application.

In practice, it is impossible to evaluate precisely the optimum dosage since oil thickness varies significantly within the slick. Concentrating on the treatment of the thickest part of the slick will result in less wasted chemical. Application rates of 50 litres/hectare have been found to be appropriate in many situations, but adjustment is necessary to compensate for any possible variation in slick thickness caused by different types of oil and environmental conditions. The application rate may be controlled by varying the discharge rate of the pumps or the speed of the vessel or aircraft.

## 8.5 Monitoring Dispersant Effectiveness

**It is important that the effectiveness of chemical dispersion is monitored continually and that the response is terminated as soon as the dispersant is no longer working.**

In clear weather conditions successful dispersion will often produce a coffee coloured plume, seen to spread under the water surface. However, visual observation of effectiveness may be impaired in poor weather conditions, in waters with a high sediment content, when dispersing pale coloured oils and in poor light. Clearly, visual monitoring is impractical at night.

For the application of dispersants to be worthwhile, the oil needs to be dispersed relatively quickly to reduce the risk of it reaching sensitive resources. A change in appearance should be visible from the air shortly after spraying.

If there is no change in oil appearance or reduction in coverage, or the dispersant runs off the oil to create a milky white plume in the water, these are signs that the dispersant is not working, see Figure 8.4. If the oil has become fragmented and widely scattered, it is unlikely that sufficient oil will be removed from the water surface by the dispersant to achieve a significant benefit.

■ **Figure 8.4: Ineffective treatment of heavy fuel oil (HFO) by dispersant is characterised by a white plume in the water. The oil remains unaffected**

■ **Using fluorometers to measure oil concentrations during a training exercise**

Effectiveness can also be monitored, using 'real-time' data on the concentration of dispersed oil in the water column, with ultraviolet fluorometry (UVF). One or more fluorometers are towed behind a sampling boat at depths of at least a metre under the slick and the variation in oil concentrations is measured. Dispersion is demonstrated by a significant increase in the concentration of oil detected by the sensor compared with that measured prior to dispersant application. However, UVF cannot provide a quantitative measurement of the amount of oil that is actually being removed from the sea surface and it should be used in combination with visual observations to decide whether a worthwhile response can be achieved.

■ A portable fluorometer that can be set up for continuous flow monitoring in the field or used in the laboratory for discrete sampling

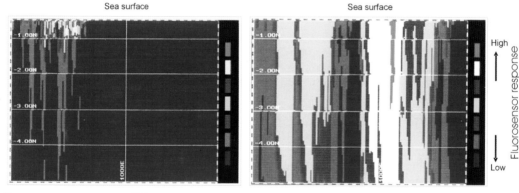

■ Fluorometer response to oil from 0.5 to 5 metres water depth under a surface slick before (left) and a few minutes after dispersant application (right). Oil rapidly disperses and dilutes to deeper than 5 metres after treatment. (Illustrations courtesy of AEA Technology)

# 8.6 Logistics and Control

Dispersant application is a specialised operation that requires preparation and trained operators. In the interests of safety and effectiveness it is necessary to use spotter aircraft to guide and coordinate spraying vessels and aircraft. The crew of the spotter aircraft should be able to identify the heavier concentrations of oil or the slicks posing the greatest threat and must have good communication with the spraying aircraft or vessel crews to guide them to the target. During the spraying operation itself, spotter aircraft can be used to judge the accuracy of the application and the effectiveness of the treatment. This is particularly important when large multi-engine aircraft are used for spraying because, from a low altitude, the crew will have great difficulty in distinguishing between oil and sheen, particularly if the slick is broken up.

To ensure safety, aircraft exclusion zones need to be in force during aerial spraying operations. Periodic checks of the aircraft are also recommended to ensure that the dispersant does not contaminate lubricants, particularly in the tail rotor of helicopters, or attack exposed rubber components of aircraft flight control systems. It is advisable to regularly wash down the aircraft with fresh water to remove both dispersant and salt water spray.

Good organisation on the ground is needed to enable spraying operations to continue for the maximum available time during daylight hours. This may require routine maintenance and transport of additional supplies of fuel and dispersant to be carried out at night. Sufficient stockpiles of dispersant should be conveniently located in order to supply vessels or aircraft with the minimum delay. Similarly, thought should be given to the provision of fuel, particularly for aircraft, and to the equipment required for reloading vessels or aircraft, such as high capacity pumps and road tankers.

In a large incident, coordination of all response actions is necessary to ensure dispersant use does not overlap or conflict with other response techniques. For example, oil dispersed into the water column cannot be contained by booms or recovered by skimmers. In addition, because of its relative surface tension, oil adheres to many sorbent materials, such as polypropylene. As the surface tension of oil is modified by dispersants, the effectiveness of sorbent materials can be significantly reduced. Oleophilic skimmers will be similarly affected when used alongside dispersants.

Image courtesy of USCG

■ **The ability to rapidly resupply and turn around aircraft for fresh sorties will assist in maximising the effectiveness of a spraying operation**

### 8.6.1  Storage

For long-term storage of dispersants, plastic drums are preferred provided that they are kept out of direct sunlight. Dispersants that are stored unopened should last for many years. However, once tanks or intermediate bulk containers are opened, the dispersant should be tested periodically for its effectiveness. Recommendations from manufacturers include an annual visual inspection together with a check of the main physical characteristics, such as density, viscosity and flash point. If these physical parameters have significantly changed or the expiry date has been reached, a dispersant effectiveness test should be conducted.

■ **Dispersant stored in 200 litre drums**

Dispersants of different types, ages or brands should not be mixed in the same tank or storage container as this may alter the viscosity of the dispersant or cause some components to precipitate or coagulate. Dispersants should not be stored after they have been diluted with sea water. The optimum storage temperature for most dispersants is between -15ºC and 30ºC and manufacturers recommend that temperature fluctuations are kept to a minimum during storage. In very cold temperatures, some dispersants may become too viscous to pass through the spray nozzles.

### 8.6.2  Using Dispersants on Shorelines

The use of dispersants on shorelines should be restricted to areas where there is strong tidal flushing because dispersed oil cannot be collected and high concentrations may harm marine organisms in the immediate vicinity. In some countries, legislation may prohibit the use of dispersants on shorelines altogether; otherwise, their use should be limited to areas of low environmental concern but high amenity value. Only regulated products should be used.

Bulk oil should first be recovered before dispersant use is considered on the shore. Dispersants are generally reserved for cleaning rocks, seawalls and other manmade structures. They are typically applied from hand operated backpack systems and brushed vigorously into the oil before flushing with sea water. Shoreline cleaners may also be used, but they are quite different products and are employed when the intention is to collect the oil released.

## 8.7 Environmental Considerations

Dispersant use has always been controversial. It may be viewed as a way of minimising potential impacts on sensitive resources by preventing or reducing shoreline contamination, but it is also sometimes seen as adding another pollutant to the environment. Despite improvements in dispersant formulations, the toxicity of the dispersant/oil mixture to marine fauna and flora is often the major environmental concern. Approval processes for dispersant use are in place in many countries and these are normally designed to take both effectiveness and toxicity into account. Products approved in one country may not be approved in another and, where available, the relevant national list should be consulted prior to application.

In open water, elevated oil concentrations are normally only observed in the upper layers of the water column (<10 metre) and are rapidly diluted by water movement. Studies have shown that oil concentrations in the range of 30-50 ppm can be expected in the top 10 metres of the water column immediately after dispersant application, diminishing to 1-10 ppm after a few hours. This means the exposure for marine organisms is acute rather than chronic and the limited exposure time reduces the likelihood of long-term adverse effects on fauna and flora. However, spraying dispersants in shallow water is inadvisable unless there is

■ **Dispersant use is not appropriate in environmentally sensitive areas such as coral reefs and seagrass beds, except in special circumstances and after careful consideration of the potential environmental consequences of using them. A balanced assessment of the net environmental and economic benefits is necessary**

sufficient water exchange to ensure adequate dilution of the dispersed oil plume.

An estimation of the dilution potential is a useful basis for making the decision on whether dispersants should be used to protect certain resources without risking undue damage to others. Relevant factors to take into account are water depth, oil quantity per unit area, the distance between the application site and sensitive areas, the direction of currents and the mixing depth of the surface waters.

By removing oil from the water surface, dispersants minimise impacts on seabirds and sensitive shorelines such as saltmarshes, mangroves and tourist beaches. However, oil removed from the surface is transferred to the water column and it is the risk of damage by dispersed oil that has to be balanced against its removal from the surface. In the case of many free swimming fish species, their ability to detect and avoid oil in the water column will help to reduce their potential exposure. However, corals, seagrass and fish spawning areas may be highly sensitive to dispersed oil and dispersants are not normally used if these resources could be affected. The use of dispersants is also generally avoided in the vicinity of fish cages, shellfish beds or other shallow water fisheries because of the increased risk of tainting. Similarly, the use of dispersants close to industrial water intakes is not advisable.

---

💧 **The factors influencing the decision to use dispersants are seldom clear cut and a balance has to be struck between the advantages and limitations of different response options (including reliance on natural processes), cost effectiveness and conflicting priorities for protecting different resources from pollution damage.**

---

Because the opportunity to use dispersants may be limited, the circumstances when dispersants may or may not be used should be agreed at the contingency planning stage to avoid delays.

## 8.8 Planning for Dispersant Use

Factors to be considered during the contingency planning process include the types of oil likely to be involved in a spill, dispersant effectiveness on these oils, sensitive resources in the area and logistics. Logistics relate mainly to the location and availability of dispersants, spraying equipment, vessels, aircraft, airstrips and refuelling capability, as well as to customs clearance for any international support required. It is unlikely that a single payload will be sufficient to treat a slick, particularly if the release is continuous, in which case sources of additional supplies of dispersant need to be identified. Sensitivity maps are particularly useful to indicate when and where dispersants may or may not be used. Thought also needs to be given to how the costs of maintaining an effective dispersant response capability should be met. The outcome of these discussions should be documented clearly in a contingency plan.

An awareness of the dispersant use policy in a particular country is also important as conflicts may arise and fines may be imposed if dispersants are used without prior consent or regard for national regulations. The competent authority may also grant pre-approvals to oil handling facilities or ports, allowing them to use dispersants without further consultation provided that certain criteria have been met.

Training and exercises are an essential part of planning for dispersant use, as they are for all aspects of spill response. Operational crews should receive comprehensive training on the various aspects of dispersant application and safety, and undertake practical exercises to mobilise resources and operate spraying equipment.

**SEA EMPRESS – Wales, UK, 1996**

Dispersants were used to combat the spill from the SEA EMPRESS, which grounded at the mouth of Milford Haven, Wales, UK, in February 1996. The bulk of the 72,000 tonnes of Forties Blend crude oil lost was released during a 4 day period during which some 445 tonnes of dispersant were applied to enhance the rate of natural dispersion. The majority of dispersant was applied using a fleet of DC-3 aircraft under contract to the UK's Marine Pollution Control Unit (part of the Department of Transport). An ADDS pack (Aerial Dispersant Delivery System) in a Hercules C130 aircraft was also used. Remote sensing planes were positioned above the spray aircraft to direct the spray pattern, which allowed the oil to be targeted effectively. As dispersants are most effective on fresh oil, the strategy was first to target significant new releases of oil leaking from the casualty after successive groundings. The secondary target was larger patches of more weathered oil further offshore. The effectiveness of the spraying was monitored after each run, using flow-through fluorometry to measure the concentration of oil at different depths below the surface. The aerial spraying operation was terminated once the patches of oil remaining on the surface were judged too small to treat effectively or had emulsified and weathered to an extent where they were no longer amenable to the use of dispersants.

It has been estimated that between 18,000–27,000 tonnes of oil spilt by the SEA EMPRESS were dispersed by the spraying operation. Even at the conservative end of the scale, this means that each tonne of dispersant resulted in at least an extra 40 tonnes of oil being dispersed, an improvement on the normally accepted planning ratio of 1:20 dispersant to oil. The effectiveness of the dispersant was due to a number of factors, including the amenability of Forties Blend crude oil to chemical dispersion and the use of surveillance aircraft to direct the operation and target the fresh oil releases. Without chemical dispersion it is estimated that at least 18,000 tonnes of oil would have remained on the sea surface and may have come ashore. Had it not dispersed, much of the oil would have emulsified, increasing its volume by a factor of three to four (i.e. 54,000-72,000 tonnes of emulsion). The result of the combined dispersant and mechanical recovery operation was that only around 10,000-15,000 tonnes of emulsion impacted the shoreline.

The main environmental impact of dispersant use at sea is that the oil is mixed through the water column, increasing the exposure of marine organisms to it. In the case of the SEA EMPRESS, the rapid large-scale use of dispersants at sea may have contributed to the stranding of bivalve molluscs and other benthic species, but none of these involved commercially exploited stock. Studies also showed that amphipods were killed in some areas, however, within five years of the spill the amphipod fauna had shown clear signs of recovery. There is no evidence of birds or mammals being affected by oil in the water column.

On balance, it appears that the use of dispersants was of overall benefit to the environment by shortening the time that oil remained on the sea surface and significantly reducing the amount of oil that could have reached the shoreline, thereby minimising the impact on birds, the intertidal zone and amenity beaches. This incident demonstrated the value of having arrangements in place for aerial dispersant spraying as part of the UK national contingency plan.

Many oil spills result in pollution of shorelines despite efforts to combat the oil at sea and to protect the coastline. The oil that reaches the coast generally has the greatest environmental and economic impact and also determines, to a large extent, the political and public perception of the scale of the incident, as well as the costs.

A combination of clean-up techniques is normally used when cleaning contaminated shorelines, including manual and mechanical removal, flushing or washing with water at high or low temperatures and pressures and wiping with rags and sorbent material. On occasions, no intervention will be required as oil on shorelines may be best left to weather and degrade naturally.

It is important to choose techniques that are appropriate for the level of contamination and shoreline type, which may range from mud flats, through sandy and cobble beaches to rocky shores and cliffs, and may include manmade structures such as breakwaters and protective walls.

> **Good organisation and management is the key to effective clean-up. Poorly thought out and uncoordinated clean-up efforts usually result in inefficient use of resources and excessive quantities of waste for disposal, and can potentially result in greater damage to the environment.**

## 9.1 Strategy

The principal objective of shoreline clean-up is to restore normal usage of the area by removing oil accumulations and enhancing natural recovery of shoreline resources, while taking care to ensure that the techniques selected do not do more harm than good. Shoreline clean-up needs to be carried out in accordance with a clear strategy that takes account of the characteristics of the oil, the level of contamination, the difficulty of access, the safety of clean-up crews and the relative environmental, economic and amenity sensitivities of different locations.

Shoreline clean-up is usually carried out in three stages:

Stage 1: Collection of floating oil and heavily contaminated beach material.

Stage 2: Removal of stranded oil and moderately oiled beach materials.

Stage 3: Final clean-up of lightly contaminated shorelines and removal of oily stains.

It may not always be necessary to progress through each of these stages and, in many situations, once Stage 2 has been completed, any remaining oil will be best left to weather and degrade naturally.

Clean-up effort should be directed to areas that have the heaviest concentrations of mobile oil

first, as the oil might otherwise move under the influence of changing winds and currents, leading to a greater length of coastline being contaminated. If oil is still leaking from the source or floating at sea, contamination of the shoreline may continue for some while. In addition, sunken oil can be remobilised by storms, thereby recontaminating areas cleaned previously.

It is usually preferable to wait until all the oil from a particular incident has come ashore before beginning beach clean-up to avoid cleaning the same area more than once. However, this must be weighed against the likelihood of the oil becoming mixed into the substrate and even buried if the clean-up is delayed too long.

■ **Stage 1 – Removal of heavy contamination**

■ **Stage 2 – Removal of moderately contaminated oiled beach material**

■ **Stage 3 – Removal of oily stains**

| | Type | Comments |
|---|---|---|
| | Rocks, boulders and manmade structures | Oil is often carried past rocky outcrops and cliffs by reflected waves, but may be thrown up onto the splash zone and accumulate on rough or porous surfaces. In tidal regions, oil collects in rock pools and may coat rocks throughout the tidal range. This oil is usually rapidly removed by wave action, but is more persistent in sheltered waters |
| | Cobbles, pebbles and shingle | Oil penetration increases with increasing substrate size. In areas with strong wave action, surface stones are cleaned quickly by abrasion whereas buried oil may persist for some time. Low viscosity oils may be flushed out of the beach by natural water movement. |
| | Sand | Particle size, water table depth and drainage characteristics determine the penetration of oil into sand beaches. Coarse sand beaches tend to shelve more steeply and dry out at low water, enabling some penetration to occur, particularly with low viscosity oils. Oil is generally concentrated near to the high water mark. Fine grained sand is usually associated with a flatter beach profile that remains wet throughout the tidal cycle so that little penetration takes place. However, some oil can be buried when exposed to surf conditions, for example, during a storm. |
| | Mud (mud flats, marshes, mangroves) | Extensive deposits of mud are characteristic of low energy environments. Little penetration of the substrate by oil occurs because the sediment is usually waterlogged but oil can persist on the surface over long periods. If the spill coincides with a storm, oil can become incorporated in the sediment and persist. Animal burrows and plant root channels can also cause oil to penetrate. |
| | Corals | Most corals are submerged at all stages of the tide and are unlikely to be affected by floating oil but, in some parts of the world, corals dry out at low water. In such cases oil adheres in much the same way as for rocky coasts and can cause serious damage to the coral and reef communities. However, the strong currents and wave conditions associated with coral reefs are likely to bring about rapid cleaning. |

■ **Table 9.1: Description of the behaviour of oil on some common types of shoreline**

The second stage of clean-up can be the most protracted part of the operation. Great care has to be taken to remove as little clean beach material with the oil as possible so that both the risk of subsequent erosion and the quantity of material for disposal are minimised. The final traces of oil are often difficult and time consuming to remove. An extensive Stage 3 clean-up is generally only required for high amenity areas during, or just before, the tourist season.

## 9.2 Clean-up Techniques

Shorelines exhibit varying degrees of sensitivity to oil pollution, depending on shoreline type. In some environments oil may persist for a long time, while in others it will be rapidly removed. A description of the behaviour of oil in different shore types is given in Table 9.1 and it can be seen that the type of shoreline largely determines the most appropriate clean-up technique. A response method that may be applied successfully to one shoreline type may be impractical or damaging to another.

Clean-up techniques may be applicable to more than one stage of a response. In particular, some techniques in Stage 2 may also be used in the first or third stages.

### 9.2.1 Rocks, Boulders and Manmade Structures

**Stage 1**
Where there is vehicular access to the water's edge the oil can be collected using skimmers, pumps, vacuum trucks or vacuum tank trailers. Many skimmers do not function well in shallow water or in the presence of waves and should only be used if they lead to enhanced oil recovery rates. The amount of oil collected by skimming/pumping at the water's edge can vary considerably and will depend on the oil thickness and encounter rate. Factors limiting the collection rate include clogging and blockages due to the presence of sediment and pressure losses caused by the viscosity of the oil.

■ **Recovery of fluid bulk oil from the shoreline using a rope mop skimmer and vacuum pumps**

Water collected with the oil should, ideally, be allowed to settle and then drained off before the oil is taken away for disposal. On tidal shorelines the oil can sometimes be concentrated at the water's edge by flushing it off the rocks or stones. Depending on

sea conditions, it may be possible to use booms to hold oil onto the shoreline during collection.

Where there is no road access close to the water's edge the oil has to be picked up manually using buckets, scoops or other containers.

Manual collection is much more selective than techniques using machinery because the amount of underlying clean material collected can be minimised. Although manual clean-up can be relatively slow, the recovery of manually cleaned shores tends to be more rapid as a result of less physical disturbance.

Because of the difficulty of manhandling containers full of oil over this type of terrain, a 'human chain' with buckets is often used to move the oil from the water's edge to temporary storage tanks located above the high water mark. Drums or other containers can sometimes be carried in small boats if these can approach the shoreline safely.

If the oil is particularly fluid it may be possible to use skimmers in nearby vessels or gather the oil with small workboats pulling short lengths of boom. If the oil is emulsified, viscous or mixed with sand, it can be loaded directly into plastic bags by hand or with shovels. Rubble or fertilizer bags, or woven polypropylene bags such as those used for rice and sugar, are most suitable to support the weight but, because of the difficulty of handling them, they should not be over-filled. Plastic bags exposed to strong sunlight for more than about 10 days will begin to deteriorate and so disposal of the filled bags should not be delayed.

Another approach is to mix the liquid oil with sorbents so that it can be handled as a solid and the sorbent/oil mixture collected with forks and rakes. Consideration should be given to the volume of waste generated using this technique and the potential additional costs of the purchase and disposal of sorbents. In the absence of synthetic products, naturally occurring local materials such as straw, palm fronds, coconut husks, bagasse (plant fibre), peat or chicken feathers can be used. In some well-publicised cases human hair has been used to create mats or booms, but disposal is an issue as the hair does not biodegrade.

**Stage 2**
In many cases, once mobile oil has been removed, the oil remaining on rocks, boulders and manmade structures can be left to weather naturally as the risk of oil spreading has been minimised. However, where rocky shores are part of the coastal amenities, further cleaning can be achieved by pressure washing. This method should only be undertaken on hard surfaces, as the pressure of the water can result in physical damage on softer surfaces. Both hot and cold water can be used, depending upon equipment availability and oil type. High temperatures and, on occasions, even steam are required to dislodge viscous oils. However, heat and high pressure will have an adverse effect on organisms and vegetation and the technique should be adjusted to suit the sensitivity of the site. It is essential that oil released through pressure washing is collected, otherwise it may pollute previously cleaned or uncontaminated

surfaces. The oil may be flushed down into a boom at the water's edge and collected with skimmers or vacuum trucks, or it may be collected by arranging sorbents at the base of the rocks being cleaned.

■ **Cleaning of rip-rap using high pressure washing**

**Stage 3**
The use of dispersants can sometimes also assist oil removal. However, in some instances, and particularly with more viscous oils, the chemical simply acts to release the oil from the rock and does not produce a dispersion. In such cases every effort should be made to collect undispersed oil to prevent recontamination. Some administrations do not permit the use of dispersants on shorelines, but where they are allowed only those products approved by national regulatory agencies should be used.

In tropical and sub-tropical environments hot water washing is likely to be less effective than in temperate climates, as oil exposed to the sun can become baked onto the rock. In this case small areas can be cleaned by sand blasting, although only where it is necessary to remove all traces of oil.

> It should be appreciated that while many marine plants and animals will survive a single oiling, the methods described above will lead to the destruction of most of the marine biota living on the rocks. Some damage to rock surfaces themselves may also occur. These methods should, therefore, only be used when absolutely necessary, such as in high amenity areas.

Further cleaning of stains left after high pressure washing operations in high amenity areas can often be achieved with a second round of pressure washing or, in some cases, by applying a citrus based de-greaser to the oil and hosing off the resulting mixture. By this stage of the clean-up the oil will be in the form of extremely thin films and so only very light applications will be required.

A thin coating of fresh oil can also be removed quite easily by scrubbing or wiping the surface of the rock with rags or sorbent materials. Rock wiping is often used as a final polishing technique after completion of all other clean-up operations or if access for high pressure washing equipment is restricted. It is used particularly in high amenity areas and tends to be favoured in countries where

labour is plentiful. However, close supervision of the workforce is required to ensure consistent progress along the shoreline. In addition, it should be noted that natural processes often achieve a faster, more efficient clean-up of stained beach material than any form of final polishing, and with far less effort.

### 9.2.2 Cobbles, Pebbles and Shingle

■ **Collection of oiled shingle into bags**

**Stage 1**
This type of shoreline is one of the most difficult to clean satisfactorily because much of the oil will have penetrated deep into the beach through spaces between the stones. The first stage of clean-up for cobble, pebble and shingle beaches is similar to that applied on rocky shores, i.e. pumping fluid oil where possible or removing it by hand. However, the poor load bearing characteristics of cobble, pebble and shingle shorelines can limit the movement of both vehicles and personnel.

In some cases the optimal approach may be to selectively remove oil saturated upper layers of pebbles or shingle, leaving the remaining oil-stained material to be washed naturally in the surf. While it is best to leave oiled cobbles on the beach, oiled mats of pebble and shingle can be manually loaded into plastic bags using shovels. For both consistency and health and safety reasons, the approximate number of shovel-loads of oiled material that should be put into each bag should be determined so that they weigh no more than 10-15 kg each. Depending on the transport means available, these can then be counted (to determine an approximate weight) and loaded into larger containers or 1 tonne bags (also known as big bags, ton-packs or jumbo bags) for removal from site.

>  Removal of stones should only be considered if it is certain that it will not cause serious beach erosion and that it will be possible to dispose of or reuse the material.

Another approach is to wash oily stones in-situ in plastic lined pits or large metal skips sunk into the beach with an oil releasing agent and water. The oil layer that forms is skimmed from the water's surface and the cobbles returned to the beach. During the SEA EMPRESS incident this technique was effective in removing the heavier contamination, but left the cobbles stained.

## Stage 2

Water at high pressure can be used to flush surface oil to the water's edge, but some of the oil will also be driven into the beach. Low pressure, high volume flushing can be useful to float the trapped oil to the surface, allowing oil to be collected in booms or pits dug parallel to the shoreline.

■ Oil is flushed into the sea where it can be contained and possibly recovered by short lengths of sorbent boom

Inevitably, some oil will remain in the beach after the stones at the surface have been cleaned, which may leach out as sheen over a period of weeks.

Another approach to consider in locations subject to vigorous winter storms is to allow the natural grinding of the stones to clean themselves of oil. In amenity areas it may be appropriate to mask or bury the oiled area with clean stones from higher up the beach, providing a clean surface over the summer for those using the beach for recreational purposes. Some weathering will occur due to summer temperatures and then, during the natural rearrangement of the beach that takes place in the winter, the oily stones will become exposed and the oil dispersed by abrasion and rough weather. This method can only be used where the beach is moderately oiled and it is not suitable for finer beach materials because the oil tends to migrate back to the surface. A further consideration is that the beach profile may be permanently altered and the natural sea defences weakened.

## Stage 3

The use of dispersants is not advisable on cobble and pebble beaches because it tends to carry the oil further into the substrate. An efficient way to remove the greasy film remaining on stones in the upper beach, which may be out of reach of normal waves or tides, is to push them into the sea or surf zone where the abrasive action caused by wave energy and suspended sediment naturally cleans them. This technique is known as surf-washing and can be achieved using manual or mechanical means. Remobilised oil may be collected using sorbents/booms or by using traps/trenches down current of the waves. This method may be inappropriate if the lower intertidal zone is very steep or if oil has penetrated to a large depth, as this would simply expose oily stones underneath the top layer. Surf-washing is most effectively used on lightly contaminated cobbles, pebbles and shingle as there is the potential for remobilised oil to recontaminate other areas. It should not be employed close to sensitive habitats, fishing grounds and shellfish beds.

 It may be several years before the beach profile is restored after surf-washing on cobble beaches as vigorous wave action is necessary to lift stones of this size back up the beach.

■ Cement mixers can be used to wash pebbles and stones

Cement mixers can also be used to wash pebbles and stones. The oiled pebbles or shingle are mixed with water and an oil releasing agent or diesel for about an hour. After the material has been agitated, the water is separated from the pebbles in the mixer and decanted into temporary holding tanks. Any oil that has separated is periodically skimmed from the surface of these tanks. For small patches of oiled stones, particularly in less accessible areas, the same effect can be achieved manually using halved oil drums or other suitable containers. Pebble washing can be effective, but it is time-consuming and may disrupt natural recovery processes. Significant quantities of oily water can also be generated, which may be expensive to dispose of.

### 9.2.3 Sand Beaches

■ Manual collection of oil from a sand beach

## Stage 1

Sand beaches are usually regarded as a valuable amenity resource and priority is given to cleaning them. Intertidal sand flats are also often biologically productive and important for commercial fisheries. Environmental considerations may, therefore, dictate the selection of methods likely to cause the least additional damage, such as those described later for muddy shores.

Recreational beaches often have good access, although on some shorelines temporary roadways may have to be constructed to allow heavy equipment onto the beach. While bulk oil can be removed relatively easily from sand beaches, a desire to clean them quickly can sometimes lead to difficulties. In a major spill a balance has to be struck between the speed with which large quantities of oil can be collected using heavy machinery and the associated increased removal of beach substrate. To a large extent this is determined by beach type. Coarse sand beaches are frequently unable to support any vehicle without its wheels or tracks sinking into the sand and causing oil to be mixed further into the beach. Worse still, vehicles driven onto the beach may become immobilised once loaded. In all cases, care must be exercised to ensure that excessive removal of sand does not result in beach erosion.

■ **Removal of bulk oil using a suction hose attached to a pump located further up the beach**

■ **Loaded vehicles can sink into soft substrates. This may cause the oil to become mixed with otherwise clean sediment further into the beach**

■ **A combination of heavy equipment and manual collection is more selective and efficient**

Manual methods must be used if there is no hard-standing at the top of the beach or if it is too far for pump or suction hoses to reach the water's edge. Oil, as well as oiled sorbents and debris, can be collected in plastic bags or dustbins and carried up the beach to above the high water mark.

Flat, hard-packed beaches may support heavy vehicles such as graders, front-end loaders and excavators to collect and remove large volumes of oil and contaminated material. Graders can be used when the oil has only penetrated a little way into the sand. The grader's blade is set to skim just below the beach surface and the oil and sand is drawn into lines parallel to the shoreline. The grader works down from the top of the beach and the collected oil is picked up by front-end loaders. The work can be carried out using front-end loaders alone, although the amount of sand picked up will then inevitably be greater.

An alternative method for tidal beaches is to flush the oil into trenches dug parallel to the water's edge. In a similar way, a pit may be dug, the oil flushed down the beach and then deflected into the hole by suitably positioned boards or bunds built of sand. Oil collecting in the trench or pit can be removed using pumps, vacuum trucks or tank trailers. This method results in some oil becoming mixed into the sand where the trenches are dug. Trenches dug in clean sand above the high water mark can be used to collect floating oil that has concentrated at the water's edge at high tide. These trenches should be lined with plastic sheeting to minimise contamination of the sand.

■ **Oil removal using heavy machinery has resulted in a high proportion of clean material and very low concentrations of oil in the waste**

## Stage 2

Moderately contaminated oily sand and debris is best removed by teams of operators working in conjunction with front-end loaders, the latter being used solely to transport the material collected to temporary storage sites at the top of the beach. Typically each worker will collect 1-2 m³ per day by this method. Front-end loaders and other heavy machinery used to pick up the oily sand directly can remove as much as 100-200 m³/day/machine, but at the expense of at least three times as much clean substrate. As a rule, the oil content of sand collected by machines is only 1-2%, while that collected manually contains 5-10% oil.

To make the most efficient use of each front-end loader, the operators should collect the oily sand in piles or, alternatively, fill bags or containers placed at intervals along the beach. To prevent oil from being spread along the beach, the front-end loader should work from the clean side as far as is possible. Vehicles equipped with low pressure tyres are generally more suitable than tracked vehicles.

Where there is no possibility of getting vehicles onto the beach the collected oily sand has to be carried off in heavy duty plastic bags. They should

not be filled completely because of the difficulty in carrying them over soft sand when full.

An alternative to removing contaminated shoreline material is to flush high volumes of water through sections of beach to release oil that has become mixed with sand.

Sea water is drawn through a high capacity pump and distributed through a number of hoses. By directing these water jets into a small area of beach the oil is floated out and flushed to the water's edge for collection. The substrate is also agitated manually to encourage the oil to separate from the sand. The method is slow and limited to the treatment of small areas at a time.

■ **Oil is flushed out of a bunded area of beach and recovered with sorbent boom**

## Stage 3

Surf washing can also be employed on exposed sand beaches and could be considered as a secondary clean-up technique depending on the amount of oil present. Contaminated sand is transferred into the surf zone, either manually or using heavy machinery, for washing on subsequent tides. The process can be repeated as necessary if the initial washing is insufficient to remove the contamination to the desired level. Surf washing is particularly useful

■ **Final clean-up of a sandy beach by ploughing**

for resolving problems with buried oil without the large-scale removal of material for disposal offsite.

■ **Lightly contaminated sand is moved into the surf zone to benefit from natural cleaning processes**

After the majority of the contaminated beach material has been removed the remaining substrate is likely to have a greasy texture and may be discoloured. Recreational beaches will require a final clean-up to restore them to their original use.

A method that is particularly appropriate for tidal beaches is to repeatedly plough or harrow the lightly oiled beach at low water. The oil is then mixed with a greater volume of sand and more frequently exposed to weathering and flushing processes. This also keeps the oiled sediments regularly aerated, allowing naturally occurring bacteria and other microorganisms to degrade the oil.

The material remaining after the clean-up of dry sand beaches is usually in the form of small nodules of oily sand (up to about 50 mm in diameter) or tarballs. It may be possible to pick out oiled debris and larger clumps of oiled sand and tarballs using beach cleaning machines, which are usually purpose built for general beach litter collection. In principle, these machines remove the top surface of the beach to a preset depth and pass the sand through a series of vibrating or rotating screens. The oily lumps are retained within the vehicle while the clean sand is allowed to drop back onto the beach. These machines may not be effective in collecting smaller tarballs.

Collection of tarballs by hand or by sieving might also be a way of reducing the quantities of clean sand removed from the beach. However, this can be extremely time consuming and should

■ **Manual collection of tarballs is selective but time consuming**

only be considered for short stretches of high amenity beaches.

On the rare occasions that it may be necessary to bring in clean sand to replace sand that has been removed it is essential that, as far as possible, the clean sand should have the same grain size as the natural material so that it behaves in a similar way. If finer grained sand were to be used as a replacement there is a risk that it might be washed away too quickly.

When sufficient notice is available before the oil reaches the beach it may be possible to move some of the sand to above the high water mark. This material can then be replaced after the beach has been cleaned.

### 9.2.4 Muddy Shores

Marsh vegetation can usually survive a single oil smothering and, in many instances, new plants grow through the covering of oil. Where removal of the oil is essential to prevent its migration elsewhere, low pressure water hoses can be used to flush the oil into open water, where it may be possible to contain it within a boom for subsequent collection. Compressed air from SCUBA diving equipment, for example, might also be used to direct floating oil away from the vegetation. These techniques are best applied by approaching the shoreline from the water in shallow draught boats or by using temporary walkways, taking care not to cause additional damage to the marsh habitat. If birds are threatened, cutting and removal of oiled vegetation might be considered, but this must be balanced against the longer term damage likely to be caused by trampling and bird hazing techniques may be more appropriate.

■ **Two months after receiving an oiling of heavy fuel oil, this salt marsh showed obvious signs of recovery**

Similar considerations apply to mangroves. If manual collection is used, this should be undertaken under close supervision to minimise additional damage to plant roots and shoots. Cutting of mangroves should be avoided, because recovery times are known to be protracted.

### Bird hazing

Bird hazing ('bird scaring') techniques can be auditory (e.g. horns and cannons), visual (e.g. scare tape and flashing buoys) or exclusion (e.g. netting), with the most effective dependent on the area to be protected, the nature of the habitat and the birdlife at risk. Overflights by small fixed-wing aircraft or helicopters have also been used effectively but care should be taken over seabird colonies, where there is a great risk of scaring birds into surface oil slicks. In all cases, consideration should be given to national and local regulations regarding bird hazing.

 **Whenever possible, it is preferable to allow oil that arrives on mud shorelines to weather naturally, particularly where it has been washed into vegetation. It has been found that, on many occasions, activities intended to clear pollution have resulted in more damage than the oil itself because of trampling and substrate erosion.**

## 9.2.5 Corals

Live corals are unlikely to become coated with oil as they are rarely exposed to the sea surface. However, should this occur, the coral is best left undisturbed so that natural recovery can take place as quickly as possible. Natural cleansing of coral platforms that dry out at low water can be assisted by flushing with sea water at low pressure to minimise the exposure of reef communities to oil. Any oil released in this way would be more easily collected from other shoreline types should it be carried ashore.

## 9.3 Organisation

While the technical aspects of dealing with oiled shorelines are clearly important, proper organisation of the workforce is vital to the success of the operation. This is particularly the case with shoreline clean-up because of the probable involvement in a major spill of a large number of different parties, including separate central, regional and local government authorities, various agencies, port and harbour authorities, terminal operators, other private companies, commercial clean-up contractors and special interest groups.

Shoreline clean-up operations should be directed from a single command centre that has all the necessary communications and other equipment. If the spill affects a wide geographical area it may be necessary to establish forward command posts, although maintaining central coordination will still be crucial.

### 9.3.1 Workforce

Shoreline clean-up is highly labour intensive and most authorities and other agencies will need to

### The Use of Sorbent Materials

Sorbent materials may have a useful role in shoreline clean-up. For example, they may assist with the recovery of liquid oil where the use of skimmers or vacuum units is not feasible, or they may be effective for retaining oil being flushed or pressure washed from rocks. They may also be used to control floating oil residues being released from sea defences, or in saltmarshes and mangroves where other techniques are impractical or imprudent. However, there have been many instances of sorbent misuse. For example, the widespread scattering of particulate sorbents or sorbent pads on oil has been seen on many occasions when simpler techniques such as manual collection, or the use of vacuum units, would have been more appropriate. The recovery of sorbent/oil mixtures may also be more difficult than simply recovering the oil itself. For example, the presence of sorbents may clog pumps and suction devices. In addition, they increase the volume of waste and some sorbent materials require specialised and costly disposal. These factors are important when determining the overall benefit that might accrue from the use of sorbents.

■ **Excessive use of sorbents significantly increases the amount of waste for disposal**

supplement their own staff to find the workforce necessary and to ensure its adequate supervision. In some cases it will be possible to employ contract labour, the unemployed, members of the armed forces or persons who are unable to pursue their normal employment because of the spill, such as fishermen. All will need to be provided with appropriate personal protective equipment, to be educated in safe and unsafe working practices, to be fed (in some cases also housed) and trained in oil spill clean-up techniques.

Supervision and control of the workforce on the shoreline is an important component of the overall response. Generally speaking, the teams allocated to specific locations should be relatively small to facilitate effective control. Supervision of the teams is crucial to ensure good productivity and that the measures taken are in accordance with the technical advice from the command team. For this reason, regular two-way communication between the command team and the supervisors is important if shoreline clean-up is to be carried out effectively and according to agreed priorities and to ensure that resources are allocated where they are most needed.

The calibre of personnel selected to take on the role of supervisor is crucial to the success of such operations. Ideally, they should be good team leaders with the ability to control workers. They need to have sufficient initiative to deal with difficulties posed by working in remote locations while, at the same time, having an awareness of when to refer problems back to the command team.

Shoreline clean-up is a physically demanding activity. In addition, the slow progress of oil removal, especially during the secondary clean-up phase, can cause the morale of the workforce to decline. Bad weather and the re-oiling of previously cleaned areas can exacerbate this problem. For these and other reasons, clean-up teams will require periods of extended rest. However, it is important that trained teams are rotated rather than replaced as the constant recruitment of new workers results in a considerable loss of productivity while each new group is trained.

### 9.3.2  Volunteers

The publicity given to a major spill can result in volunteers travelling considerable distances to the spill site to offer their assistance with the clean-up, often prompted by a compassion for oiled wildlife or a wish to speed up the recovery of contaminated coastlines. A large number of well intentioned and enthusiastic people who are prepared to work for free would seem to be good thing, but oil spill clean-up can be complex and properly trained and informed workers are preferred. In addition, there are health and safety issues that will prevent the involvement of volunteers in hazardous areas, such as rocky shores. Also, there is a need to provide meals, tools, materials, protective clothing, sanitation, transportation and supervision. That said, the use of volunteers can be more than just a public relations exercise if their participation is properly planned and handled. A widely recognised method of utilising volunteers has been to use them for non-oil recovery functions or as support for wildlife rehabilitation activities and this has, for the most part, been successful.

■ **Volunteers often arrive in large numbers at a spill site and are usually untrained in oil spill clean-up**

### 9.3.3  Equipment Requirements

A variety of equipment, both specialised and non-specialised, will be required during a major shoreline clean-up operation. Much of the non-specialised equipment (e.g. vacuum trucks and earth moving equipment), as well as some specialised oil spill clean-up equipment and materials, will normally be available from local sources. However, in a major spill supplementary stocks of specialised equipment may have to be brought in from further afield. Sources could include stockpiles maintained by the government of the affected country, or stockpiles held by neighbouring countries, the oil industry, manufacturers or clean-up contractors.

■ **Supervision and control of the work force is essential to ensure that operations are directed to the right areas**

Obtaining sufficient equipment and materials is rarely a major problem in most spills. Ensuring that it is correctly shared between the various authorities and deployed according to technical need can be a far bigger challenge. If the spill remains at sea for some time before coming ashore, potentially threatening a long length of coast, then political, commercial and public pressures may result in equipment being deployed to the wrong areas or being too thinly spread out to do much good.

Attention should be given to the organisation of equipment and vehicles in much the same way as the workforce. Vehicles working on the beach should be confined to the work area while larger capacity lorries transporting the collected material to storage or disposal sites should be kept off the beach so that dirty and clean areas remain segregated. This not only limits the number of vehicles involved, but also helps to reduce the amount of oil spilling onto the roads. Road traffic in the vicinity of the work site should be controlled so that the movement of trucks into and out of the work site is not hindered. The beach may also have to be closed in the interests of public safety, particularly where heavy vehicles are being used.

---

**HEBEI SPIRIT – Republic of Korea, 2007**

On 7 December 2007, the fully laden tanker HEBEI SPIRIT was struck by a crane barge while at anchor 5 miles off Taean, on the west coast of the Republic of Korea, spilling 10,900 tonnes of crude oil.

The oil polluted a 400 km stretch of coastline to varying degrees. This comprised a wide range of shore types; long sand amenity beaches, muddy shores and rocky inaccessible cliffs, as well as manmade structures, such as harbours and sea walls. A major shoreline clean-up operation was launched, which involved 21 separate clean-up contractor companies, numerous city authorities hiring many local villagers as labourers (up to 10,000 people a day) and significant numbers from the army and navy. A large number of volunteers (up to 50,000 a day) from all over Korea also participated in the clean-up operations. In total, more than one million man-days were worked during the first two months after the spill. The removal of the bulk oil was achieved primarily using the large workforce to remove the oil with buckets, shovels and sorbent pads. At selected sites, contractors also used vacuum trucks, skimmers and mechanical means. Secondary clean-up measures involved surf washing, flushing and hot water high-pressure treatment. Widespread manual wiping of rocks and pebbles using sorbent materials and other textiles was also carried out.

Despite operational efficiency being hampered by logistical problems such as the harsh winter weather, strong currents and steep rocky shorelines, most of the bulk oil had been removed within a couple of months and secondary clean-up operations were for the most part completed by the end of June 2008. Some clean-up in remote areas continued until October 2008.

---

Tracking the movement of equipment and materials, especially those purchased or obtained under contract, can also sometimes prove difficult in a major operation. Daily records of the personnel and equipment working in each area should be kept and are essential for the formulation of subsequent claims for compensation. A record of the quantity of oil and oily debris being removed and sent for disposal or treatment enables progress to be monitored more easily and may highlight problem areas early.

# 9.4 Termination of Clean-up

The decision to bring shoreline operations to a close depends on a wide range of different considerations, such as the importance given to the area, the time of year and the rate at which natural cleaning is expected to take place. Often there are conflicting concerns to be resolved and overcome. The most frequently encountered conflict arises from a demand to remove every last drop of oil from the shoreline. This may be driven by a desire to repair the damage caused by a manmade accident or it may be politically motivated. However, complete removal is neither achievable nor necessary and does not recognise the capacity of the natural environment to recover relatively quickly from perturbations such as oil spills.

Another common area of conflict is between environmental concerns and economic interests such as tourism. Those responsible for managing amenity resources for the tourist industry are likely to demand that the clean-up is completed as quickly as possible, especially if the incident occurs during, or just prior to, the tourist season. This usually leads to the use of more aggressive clean-up techniques with less consideration of the risk of damage these measures may themselves cause to environmentally sensitive resources and fisheries.

Net Environmental and Economic Benefit Analysis (NEEBA) is a process that considers the potential for continued clean-up to cause more damage than the original oil spill. NEEBA balances sensitivities (in either ecological or socioeconomic terms) to determine the most appropriate techniques and level of cleanliness. Decisions on sensitivities are made easier if environmental and socioeconomic priorities are addressed during the preparation of oil spill contingency plans, with consultation and agreement with all relevant parties.

Another factor influencing the decision to stop cleaning is the cost. Expenditure escalates dramatically through the three stages of shoreline clean-up. As the work progresses it becomes more and more difficult and requires ever-increasing effort to remove the diminishing amounts of oil. At some point the costs become disproportionate to the benefits that can be derived from further cleaning.

Determining the objectives of the clean-up operation at an early stage will be of assistance as these discussions are likely to dictate the clean-up strategy and techniques to be used. Furthermore, obtaining agreement on the criteria for terminating the clean-up at the beginning of the operation will facilitate discussion of what may be a difficult decision.

## AMORGOS – Taiwan, 2001

The bulk carrier AMORGOS suffered engine failure and grounded off the southern tip of Taiwan in January 2001. Shortly afterwards, the vessel began to break up and an estimated 1,000 tonnes of fuel oil (IFO 180) was lost, stranding along approximately 5 km of fossilised coral shoreline within the Kenting National Park, a protected area and tourist attraction. The shore is backed by dense vegetation and steep, rugged cliffs 50-100 metres high.

The hostile conditions and remoteness of the area where the oil stranded made clean-up particularly difficult. No vehicular access to the shoreline was possible and much of the clean-up was carried out manually by the local villagers, with assistance from the Taiwanese army. The removal of bulk oil took eight weeks and involved collecting oil from the water's edge in buckets and passing it along human chains to staging areas before pumping it up the cliff face.

A range of secondary cleaning techniques was evaluated for the difficult task of removing residual oil from the heavily pitted rock formations, taking into account the most sensitive areas in the immediate sub-tidal zone where coral veneer was present. Close to the surf zone and in areas exposed to regular strong wave action, natural cleaning was evident within just a few weeks. For many less exposed areas, however, it was clear that little improvement would be likely without secondary cleaning. The presence of corals in shallow waters next to the shore precluded the use of chemical cleaning agents. Eventually, agreement was reached with the national authorities to use hot water pressure washing but, because of the environmental impacts that would inevitably result, clean-up was kept to a minimum. One area of high amenity value, visible from a designated viewpoint, was cleaned extensively. Elsewhere, cleaning was restricted to the upper shore and sheltered areas where waves were unlikely to promote self-cleaning. The oil washed off in the cleaning process was collected using locally made sorbents.

Once the heavy accumulations of oil had been removed, the shoreline could arguably have been left to clean naturally, given its exposed setting, but this was a shoreline of high national importance both for its diversity and tourism value and a compromise had to be found. A balance needed to be struck between the clean-up operations causing damage to the corals and the need to restore the aesthetic appearance of the shoreline.

■ **A human chain moving oil from the water's edge**

# DISPOSAL OF OIL AND OILED WASTE

**10**

Most oil spill clean-up operations, particularly those on shore, result in the collection of substantial quantities of oil and oily waste. Details of disposal options and routes should be clearly highlighted in the appropriate contingency plan and decisions on waste management should be made at the outset of an incident.

The amount of waste generated is dependent on many factors, not least the type and amount of oil spilt and the extent to which the oil spreads and affects lengths of the shoreline. The choice of response technique is also important and, where possible, preference should be given to methods that generate the minimum amount of waste for disposal. Cleaning and re-using equipment or protective clothing and sensible use of consumable resources, notably sorbent material, will also serve to reduce waste. However, even when employing appropriate and reasonable response methods, the volume of waste generated can be in the order of ten times the volume of oil spilt.

> Experience from many incidents has shown that the treatment and disposal of waste is often the most expensive and time consuming component of a response operation.

■ **Consideration should be given to the minimisation of waste: PPE should be cleaned and reused where possible**

Ideally, as much of the collected oil as possible should be recycled, for example, by reprocessing at an oil refinery. Unfortunately, this is often not possible due to weathering of the oil and contamination with debris; therefore, some form of disposal is usually required, either by direct dumping (landfill), incineration, stabilisation for use in land reclamation or road foundations, land farming or composting. The disposal option chosen will depend upon the amount and type of waste, the likely costs involved and any environmental, legal or practical limitations. In the case of large spills it may be necessary to store waste for some time before it can be dealt with.

## 10.1 Contingency Planning

> The large amounts of waste that can be collected during the clean-up of an oil spill can become a major problem if the question of disposal is not dealt with at the contingency planning stage.

A contingency plan should include details of the potential disposal options available for different amounts and types of oily material. Plans should be local in nature as the methods adopted will largely depend on the availability of raw materials and suitable disposal sites close to the spill. The facilities available may also have a bearing on the clean-up techniques employed, particularly on shorelines. Authorities should establish the capabilities of local refineries and contractors specialising in oil recovery and/or processing. Temporary storage sites should be identified at an early stage as all final disposal routes are likely to have limited capacities in relation to the rate at which the oil is collected. Following a major spill, it is unlikely that any single technique will be capable of dealing with the quantities of waste to be handled. If sufficient temporary storage can be found the problem of disposal can be approached in stages, so that the capacity of each disposal route is not overwhelmed.

Disposal can easily become a major problem and is often directly related to the amount of debris in the waste. For local plans, a survey of the coastline and identification of the debris collecting points will often indicate where spilt oil is likely to come ashore. Debris can often be removed, before the arrival of oil, at a nominal cost. Alternatively, it might be treated as a sensitive site, where a technique such as protective booming would be considered to minimise the chance of oil stranding there.

### SEA EMPRESS – Wales, UK, 1996

When the SEA EMPRESS ran aground in the entrance to Milford Haven, Wales, UK in February 1996, it spilt a total of 72,000 tonnes of crude oil over a period of seven days. The clean-up operation generated about 20,000 tonnes of liquid waste and 12,500 tonnes of oiled sand and beach materials such as seaweed, debris and protective clothing. Legislation governing the disposal of oil contaminated waste had been updated since the writing of the local authority emergency plan and disposal options that had been used previously were no longer available. In addition, the logistics of handling large quantities of waste proved challenging.

A temporary storage pit for almost 3,000 tonnes of oiled beach material was constructed in the sand dunes behind the contaminated beaches and left to biodegrade naturally. Additional oily waste was stored in a nearby warehouse. Final disposal of the oiled beach material proved difficult, in part because of the mixture of materials contained in the waste.

The majority of the oiled sand was treated by land farming at the oil refinery in Milford Haven, where conditions were maintained to promote the biodegradation of oil. The remainder of the waste was transported to a landfill site 160 km away. As a trial, a small amount of oiled sand was stabilised and used to make asphalt and a further amount was subjected to 'thermal desorption', whereby the sand was heated to burn off the hydrocarbons, which in theory would allow it to be returned to the beach.

Most of the liquid waste (collected during the mechanical recovery at sea and during the bulk oil removal operations) was taken to the refinery for processing and approximately 1,500 tonnes of oil was recovered.

This incident highlighted the importance of a regional and national strategy for dealing with waste from a major oil spill. In the case of the SEA EMPRESS, the role of the oil company in providing their facilities to handle the waste and provide final disposal options was instrumental in alleviating problems that could otherwise have slowed the rate of clean-up.

## 10.2 Nature of Oil and Oiled Material

As a general rule, spills of persistent oils such as crude, heavier grades of fuel oil and some lubricants, are most likely to give rise to treatment and disposal problems. If the oil can be collected soon after being spilt it is likely to be fluid and relatively free of contamination. In most cases, however, waste oil will be viscous due to weathering. Oil collected directly from the sea will be relatively free of solid debris, but is likely to be accompanied by a significant amount of water, depending on the collection technique. Large volumes of water may also be present as water-in-oil emulsion.

■ **Oil and debris stranded in mangroves**

Oil recovered from the shore will usually be mixed with considerable amounts of solid material, such as sand, wood, plastics and seaweed, and it will often be difficult to separate the oil into a form suitable for recycling. Oiled materials from response operations, such as sorbent boom and protective clothing, or contaminated fishing gear or mariculture facilities, can also contribute significantly to the volume of waste produced following an oil spill.

|  | Type of Material | Separation Methods | Disposal Options |
|---|---|---|---|
| **Liquids** | Non-emulsified oils and waste water | • Settling/gravity separation of free water<br>• recovered water may require further treatment/filtration | • Use of recovered oil as fuel or refinery feedstock<br>• return treated water to source |
| | Emulsified oils | Emulsion broken to release water by:<br>• Heat treatment<br>• emulsion-breaking chemicals | • Use of recovered oil as fuel or refinery feedstock<br>• stabilisation and reuse<br>• incineration |
| **Solids** | Oil mixed with sand | • Collection of liquid oil leaching from sand during temporary storage<br>• extraction of oil from sand by washing with water or solvent<br>• removal of solid oil or tarballs by sieving | • Use of recovered liquid oil as fuel or refinery feedstock<br>• recycle extracted water/solvent<br>• stabilisation and reuse<br>• degradation through land farming or composting<br>• landfill<br>• incineration |
| | Oil mixed with cobbles, pebbles or shingle | • Collection of liquid oil leaching from beach material during temporary storage<br>• extraction of oil from beach material by washing with water or solvent | • Return cleaned stones to source<br>• stabilisation and reuse<br>• landfill |
| | Oil mixed with wood, plastics, seaweed, shellfish and sorbents<br><br>Oiled fishing equipment and stock – nets, floats and racks | • Collection of liquid oil leaching during temporary storage<br>• flushing of oil from debris with water<br>• removal of free water<br>• compression | • Stabilisation and reuse following removal of plastics and large debris<br>• degradation through land-farming or composting for oil mixed with seaweed, shellfish or natural sorbents<br>• landfill<br>• incineration |
| | Tarballs | • Separation from sand by sieving | • Stabilisation and reuse<br>• landfill<br>• incineration |

■ **Table 10.1: Options for separation and disposal of oil and debris**

Each type of waste may require a different method of treatment and disposal, as indicated in Table 10.1 and, as far as possible, should be collected and stored separately. Loss of control at any stage of the disposal or treatment route can lead to additional complications and costs.

# 10.3 Storage and Preparation for Disposal

The large volumes of material requiring disposal following clean-up can often present major logistical problems in handling and transportation. It is usually necessary, therefore, to store the material temporarily to provide a buffer between collection and final disposal and to allow time to select the appropriate disposal method.

Waste from shoreline clean-up is often stored at the back of the beach above the high water mark, which enables the transportation to be undertaken in two stages; from the beach to temporary storage and then, at some future time, from temporary storage to the disposal site. This reduces the risk of contamination of roads by restricting vehicles involved in the first stage to the beach.

■ **Recovered oil transferred from a skip to a larger tank prior to heating and subsequent transfer to a processing facility**

■ **Temporary storage of plastic bags containing oiled material at the back of a beach**

Where possible, bulk oil should be stored separately from oily debris so that different methods of treatment and disposal can be used. Provided the oil is pumpable at ambient temperatures it can be stored in enclosed tanks. However, care should be exercised in the bulk storage of more viscous materials, particularly if the tanks are not fitted with heating coils as it may prove difficult to empty them. Highly viscous oils are better stored in open containers, such as barges, skips or drums, to facilitate treatment and transfer operations. If waste oil is to be stored for a significant length of time, it is essential to cover the containers to prevent spillage or rainwater infiltration. If purpose built containers are not available, bulk oil from shorelines can often be held within compacted earth walls or in simple storage pits lined with heavy gauge polyethylene (or other suitable oil-proof material) to prevent

leachate from contaminating the substrate. Long narrow storage pits, approximately 2 m wide and 1.5 m deep, are preferable to maintain ready access to all parts of the pit. However, the size of the pit should reflect the volume of waste expected. If there is the possibility of heavy rainfall, allowance should be made for this when filling the pits to ensure that oil does not flow over the top, causing further contamination. Where temporary storage of bulk oil is required in sensitive areas such as sand dunes, it is important to avoid disturbance of the stabilising vegetation as this could lead to erosion. Wherever dug, pits should be filled in after complete removal of the oil and, as far as possible, the area restored to its original state.

Security of temporary waste storage areas should be appropriate according to the risks associated with unauthorised access. Security might range from signage and roped off areas, to more impenetrable fencing and 24-hour surveillance.

Plastic bags should be regarded as a means of transporting oily material rather than for storage as they tend to deteriorate under the effect of sunlight, releasing their contents. It should also be borne in mind that, if the contents are ultimately to be treated in some way prior to disposal, it will usually be necessary to empty the bags and dispose of them separately.

Transport of material to a disposal site can become a major cost item and, where possible, the amount of material to be transported should be reduced by separating oil from water and sand during temporary storage.

 Oily waste must be stored and transported in accordance with local regulations. It is good practice to record details of the quantities and types of oily waste collected. Records will also be useful in any subsequent claims for compensation.

■ **A well lined storage pit, but poorly segregated oily waste**

## 10.4 Minimisation of Waste

The problems associated with disposal will be reduced if priority is given to minimising the amount of waste generated during the response.

Recovery of oil from contaminated beach material may be possible; for example, oil seeping from heaped debris can be collected in a ditch or bund surrounding the storage area. Alternatively, oiled beach material could be washed with water, sometimes in conjunction with a suitable solvent such as diesel or a citrus based cleaner to release the oil. Washing can also be carried out using low pressure hoses to loosen and lift off oil from debris contained in a temporary storage pit. The resulting oil/water mixture can then be pumped into tanks and the oil separated by gravity. Another approach is to wash contaminated sediment on a grill or wire mesh, with the oily water draining into a skip or tank positioned beneath.

Separation can also be achieved in a closed system using water or a solvent. Devices have been developed based on a range of equipment from standard cement mixers for small-scale batch operations to mineral processing equipment for large-scale continuous treatment. Although these large-scale systems have proved successful in specific circumstances, they have not yet found widespread application in oil spill response.

On tourist beaches, where a high standard of cleanliness may be required, the volume of waste can be reduced by separating oil, in the form of tarballs, from clean sand by selective manual clean-up. Sieving devices, both static and mechanical, are sometimes used to remove oily sand residues and tarballs from lightly contaminated sand.

■ **An improvised waste filtration system, where recovered oil is passed through a grilled funnel to filter out debris**

 The cost of cleaning large amounts of oiled beach material on site could compare favourably with other methods that involve transporting the material some distance from the coast.

In many incidents, a large percentage of the waste generated is synthetic sorbent material and a significant proportion of this is often lightly oiled. Waste problems will be reduced if sorbent is used only when other techniques are unsuitable and if care is taken to ensure that it is used to its full capacity.

## 10.5 Recovery of Oils

Under some circumstances it may be possible to recover the oil for eventual processing or blending with fuel oils for subsequent use. This process makes use of the calorific properties of the oil and has the potential to generate financial income from its sale to offset the costs of disposal. This should always be the first option to consider. Possible recipients for processing or blending are refineries, oil recovery contractors who specialise in recycling waste oils, power stations and cement works. However, strict criteria will usually have to be met before waste oils can be accepted. Generally, the oil should be pumpable, contain few solids or debris and have a relatively low salt content to minimise corrosion. Assuming that the oil is suitable for recycling, it is possible that the potential refiners or other users will not have much spare storage or processing capacity and alternative intermediate storage may be required. Tanker deballasting stations and slop reception facilities may be appropriate in this regard, but may also have limited capacity.

■ **Oil with a low water, debris and salt content may be suitable for reprocessing**

Oil collected from the sea will be most suitable for processing since it will usually only be necessary to separate any water associated with it. For free water, this separation can frequently be achieved by gravity, either in collection devices such as vacuum trucks or in tanks onboard skimming vessels, the water being removed by pumping or running off the bottom layer.

The extraction of water from water-in-oil emulsions will be more difficult. Unstable emulsions may be broken by heat treatment to a maximum temperature of 80°C, allowing the oil and water to separate by gravity. In warm climates the heat of the sun may be sufficient. More stable emulsions may require the use of chemicals known as 'emulsion breakers' or 'demulsifiers', which also tend to reduce the viscosity of most oils, rendering

them more pumpable. An exception to this is emulsion produced from heavy fuel oil under cold conditions which, although more viscous than the oil alone, is often easier to pump. There is no single chemical suitable for all types of emulsion and it may be necessary to carry out trials on site to determine the most effective agent and optimum dose rate. However, typical dose rates are in the range of 0.1–0.5% of the bulk volume to be treated. Treatment should be carried out during transfer of the emulsion from the collection device to a tank, or from one tank to another, to ensure good mixing and minimum dose rate. The emulsion breaker can be injected into the inlet side of a pump or into an in-line static mixer incorporated into a vacuum intake. After separation the water phase will contain most of the emulsion breaker and up to 0.1% of oil, so care should be exercised when disposing of it.

---

### ERIKA – France, 1999

The tanker ERIKA, carrying 31,000 tonnes of heavy fuel oil as cargo, broke in two in a severe storm in the Bay of Biscay on 11 December 1999, 60 miles from the coast of Brittany. About 20,000 tonnes of oil were spilt, affecting some 400 km of shoreline.

During the clean-up operation, more than 250,000 tonnes of oily waste – over ten times the original spill volume – was collected from shorelines and temporarily stockpiled. Temporary reception facilities were established in car parks and stretches of land close to beaches, mainly by building earth or sand bunds or digging holes and lining them with plastic.

Ultimately, the French oil company and charterer of the vessel, Total, agreed to receive all the wastes at their Donges refinery, where adequate storage sites were available within and close to the refinery.

In the early days, as many as 300 trucks per day queued up at the Donges Refinery gate. Due to the rate at which oily waste was arriving, little attention was paid to maintaining the segregation of the material. The result was a mixture of oil, sand, debris, seaweed, protective clothing, damaged booms and other response equipment such as scrapers, buckets and spades, which needed sorting before disposal could proceed. It took about six months to classify the waste and to select an appropriate treatment process. The treatment involved mechanical sorting and washing with diesel and cold water supplied by the refinery. Sand and gravel were then separated by sand screening for reuse as road or building materials; macro-waste such as plastics and wood, that remained after mechanical and manual sorting was washed and crushed and then incinerated as regular industrial waste; sludge was upgraded for use as a filling material after thermal treatment; fuel oil was recycled in the refinery and water was returned to the waste water treatment station. The waste disposal operation was completed by 2004.

---

## 10.6 Landfill

Disposal of oily waste to designated landfill sites is a commonly used disposal method. Landfill sites are often licensed under specific conditions and acceptance of waste may be limited to certain types or volumes of waste or to waste where the concentration of contaminant is below a certain threshold. In most situations, oil contaminated waste will need to be disposed of in a site that has been designated for hazardous refuse.

Modern sites are usually enclosed by an impermeable membrane to prevent substances from leaching out. In parts of the world where such linings are not regularly used, care is needed to ensure that contamination of nearby ground and surface water does not occur.

Materials intended for landfill should have a low oil content (up to a maximum of about 20%) to limit the risk of oil leaching from the site. Leachate is also reduced by the co-disposal of oily waste with domestic refuse. Even though degradation of the oil is likely to be slow through lack of oxygen, oil appears to remain firmly absorbed by all types of domestic waste. The oily waste should be deposited in cells on top of at least 4 m of domestic refuse, either in surface strips 0.1 m thick or in trenches 0.5 m deep to allow free drainage of water. The oily material should be covered by a minimum of 2 m of domestic waste to prevent oil from coming to the surface when subjected to compression from site vehicles.

Where available, disused quarries often make satisfactory disposal sites. However, they are often impermeable to water and it is important to ensure that the quarry is deep enough to prevent the overflow of any accumulated rain water, which could transfer oil outside the site.

In some countries, landfilling is now restricted by legislation. The difficulty of locating new sites and high taxation for those depositing waste is encouraging responders to look at alternative disposal options. As a result, solutions that were previously seen as prohibitively expensive, such as incineration, are becoming more economically viable.

## 10.7 Incineration

When oil is first spilt it is a flammable material. However, within a few hours at sea it loses any volatile components and picks up a high proportion of water. Burning the oil without first removing the water is very difficult and, in any case, the direct burning of uncontained oil or oily debris is not recommended, except in very remote areas, because of the smoke plume. When oil is burnt by this method it also tends to spread and be absorbed into the ground. In addition, a tar-like residue may remain as it is rarely possible to achieve complete combustion.

These problems can be overcome by using an incinerator, which destroys the waste by controlled burning at high temperatures. A number of portable incinerators have been developed for use on site in remote locations. Kilns can also be assembled from low cost materials such as 45 gallon drums, which can handle small quantities of oil contaminated beach material. However, local legislation and environmental concerns may prohibit the use of such devices.

■ **Sacks of oily waste being fed into the loading chute of a large industrial incinerator**

On a larger scale, cement factories and industrial kilns are an effective way of incinerating oily waste, subject to technical constraints such as the content of heavy metals, chlorine or sulphur. Co-incineration in a cement works is also a cost effective method of disposal as waste with an adequate calorific value can be used as a substitute for fuel that would otherwise be needed to fire the kiln. In addition, the ash resulting from waste combustion provides aluminium, silica, clay and other minerals typically added in the cement raw material feed stream. The drawback to this method, in addition to the restrictions on the type of oily waste accepted, is that cement works are often located far from the shoreline, so transportation costs must be considered.

As a general rule, incinerators used for domestic waste are not suitable for disposal of large amounts of oil as chlorides from sea water may cause corrosion. However, co-disposal of small amounts of oily waste with other refuse may be acceptable in some countries. Oiled PPE, sorbents, nettings or other materials that do not contain a high oil content are most appropriately dealt with in this way.

High temperature industrial waste incinerators, while likely to tolerate salts, are limited in supply and may not have sufficient capacity to deal immediately with the additional burden created by a large quantity of oily waste. However, if long-term storage that would allow oily waste to be incorporated into the waste stream gradually is available, this may be an acceptable route.

Another thermal process that has been used during a major incident is pyrolysis, which involves thermally degrading the waste into gas and solid residues in the absence of oxygen. Again, this is a specialised and expensive process and facilities are limited.

 The costs of incineration can be considerably higher than other techniques and this should be taken into account if this method of disposal is selected. Co-incineration in cement works reduces the costs, as treated waste can sometimes be used as a raw material or for power generation.

## 10.8 Stabilisation

■ **Stabilisation of oily waste using quicklime**

An approach that can sometimes be used with oily sand, provided that it does not contain large amounts of wood and seaweed, is to bind the material with an inorganic substance such as quicklime (calcium oxide). This forms an inert product that does not allow the oil to leach out. It will typically be in solid block form or can be granulated or powdered. The stabilised material can be disposed of under less stringent conditions than unstabilised oily sand, and can also be used for land reclamation and road construction where there is not a requirement for high load-bearing properties. Although quicklime appears to be the best binding agent, other materials such as cement and pulverised fuel ash waste from coal fired power stations might be suitable. There are also a number of commercial products, based on the same raw materials, that have been treated with various chemicals to improve their efficacy. Practical experience at spills so far suggests that these are not as cost effective as the basic raw materials themselves.

One advantage of quicklime over other materials is that the heat generated by its reaction with water in the waste reduces the viscosity of the oil, which facilitates absorption. Clearly, the suitability of the technique depends on a plentiful supply of stabilising material close to the spill location. Quicklime can usually be obtained from cement works.

The optimum amount of binding agent required is dependent primarily on the water content of the waste rather than the amount of oil, which should be determined experimentally on site. However, for quicklime the amount required is typically 5 – 30% of the weight of the bulk material to be treated. Treatment can be carried out at a central facility or at the site of a spill.

At a treatment centre, the agent would be mixed with the waste in a continuous process. This method requires the use of expensive equipment, including a drum mixer. Smaller quantities could be treated in a batch process using standard concrete mixers.

Alternatively, waste can be spread out in treatment beds at the final disposal site in layers up to 30 cm thick and mixed using a pulverising mixer, which incorporates the lime. Following treatment the wastes are left in place and either covered over or landfilled. This is a more cost effective method provided there is sufficient land available.

On occasions, it may be preferable to carry out primary mixing in pits at the site of the spill, either manually or using a bulldozer or mechanical shovel. This renders the oiled material more suitable for transport and final treatment can then be undertaken at a larger reception facility using specialised equipment. The technique creates a great deal of corrosive dust so, if possible, the treatment site should be selected to minimise its spread to adjacent property. It is also important that operating personnel wear protective clothing and face masks to protect skin, lungs and eyes. If, after mixing, the material is to be utilised in construction it is essential to compact it using road building equipment.

# 10.9 Land Farming

Oil and oily waste can sometimes be broken down using biological processes, but at a rate that is often too slow to benefit most spill response applications. Bioremediation is the term used for methods that accelerate the microbial breakdown of oil. One such technique is land farming, whereby the oil and debris is spread over an area of land set aside for the purpose. For many years, oil refineries around the world constructed land farms to deal with oily wastes, but increasingly sites suitable for bioremediation are becoming difficult to find.

Land farming is only likely to be applicable to relatively small spills because of the large amount of land required. The contaminated material should have a relatively low oil content and, ideally, the land selected should be of low value, located well away from drinking water supplies and should not be permeable.

The top soil should first be loosened by means of a harrow and the area bunded to contain any oil runoff. The oily debris is then spread over the surface to a depth of no more than 20 cm, the maximum application rate being about 400 tonnes of oil per hectare of land. The oil should be left to weather until it is no longer sticky, before being thoroughly mixed in with the soil using a plough or rotovator. Mixing should be repeated at intervals to increase aeration and hence the rate of biodegradation. Fertilizers may also be added to enhance biodegradation rates.

If land farming techniques are employed, the use of natural sorbents such as straw and bark during clean-up are preferable to synthetic materials, as natural sorbents break down more rapidly. Large items of debris, such as timber and boulders, should be removed. Once most of the oil has degraded the soil should be capable of supporting a wide variety of plants, including trees and grasses.

# 10.10 Composting

Another effective means of enhancing degradation is to employ composting techniques, particularly if natural sorbents such as straw, peat and bark have been used. Provided the mixtures contain relatively low levels of oil, they can be stacked into heaps to facilitate composting. Because the heaps retain heat the technique is particularly suitable in colder climates, where degradation through land farming is slow. However, it is only applicable for small scale operations.

 Although a variety of techniques have been developed for dealing with oil and oily wastes, many have limited application and capacity. In the event of a major spill, all options need to be considered.

|  | Benefits | Disadvantages |
|---|---|---|
| Reprocessing | • Recycling through use of the calorific properties of the oil<br>• permanent storage not required | • Oiled waste may require treatment before processing<br>• facilities and processing capacity are limited<br>• long-term storage of waste may be required while awaiting processing |
| Landfill | • Organic waste may biodegrade naturally at a landfill<br>• can rapidly deal with large amounts of waste | • Restricted application dependent on local legislation<br>• sites designated for hazardous waste are scarce and can charge high rates<br>• many types of waste likely to persist for a long time |
| Incineration | • Can be employed for many types of oiled material<br>• permanent storage not required | • Relatively expensive disposal process<br>• appropriate facilities and processing capacity are limited<br>• long-term storage of waste may be required |
| Stabilisation | • National legislation often allows for easier disposal of stabilised oiled material<br>• recycling through use of stabilised oiled material in construction | • Only appropriate for oiled sand, shingle and pebbles with debris of limited size<br>• treatment of oiled material requires skilled personnel and suitable reception facilities and equipment |
| Land farming or composting | • Enhances natural process of biodegradation | • Suitable sites are increasingly difficult to find<br>• only applicable to relatively small spills because of the large area of land required<br>• not all oil components may be degraded<br>• slow process, requiring periodic tilling and monitoring |

■ Table 10.2: A summary of the benefits and disadvantages of the options typically available for treatment and disposal of oil and debris

An emergency operation, such as dealing with an oil spill, will involve many organisations and has the potential to affect a large number of people. For example, an incident involving a ship in distress may entail search and rescue, lightering of cargo and salvage activities, all of which may impinge upon the clean-up operation. There is often concern for the effects on the environment, fisheries, industry and recreation, as well as considerations of public and responder health and safety. There will inevitably be conflicting interests and such situations are easier to resolve when a well prepared and tested contingency plan is in place.

■ A major response will involve personnel from many different agencies and companies

The effectiveness of the response to an oil spill will ultimately depend upon the quality of the contingency plan and of the organisation and control of the various aspects of the clean-up operation.

## 11.1 Scope of Contingency Plans

A contingency plan should outline the overall strategy for spill response as well as the operational procedures to be followed when a spill occurs. The process of producing a plan provides the opportunity to identify roles and responsibilities and to define response strategies and procedures without the intense pressures that inevitably apply at the time of an incident. It also serves to raise awareness of the issues likely to arise in a response. For this reason, a plan should be drawn up by those who will rely on it when a spill occurs.

While every plan has a similar aim, individual plans should also reflect the culture within the country in which they will be implemented and should be working documents that are concise, accessible and easily updated. Plans should be reasonably self contained with minimal reference to other publications as this could delay decision-making.

 **Contingency planning often follows the concept of tiered response. This is a widely accepted and convenient way to categorise response levels and provides a practical basis for planning.**

■ An oil spill is easier to deal with if proper contingency plans are in place

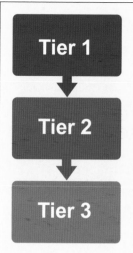

**Tier 1** — **Small spills:** typically operational spills occurring at individual ports or oil handling facilities. The company that owns the facility would usually provide the personnel and equipment for responding to this type of incident.

**Tier 2** — **Medium spills:** comprise larger spills in the vicinity of a company's facility, smaller incidents in remote locations away from operational centres and spills from shipping accidents within ports, harbours or estuaries or along a stretch of coast. Such spills require the pooling of resources by companies, industries and possibly government agencies.

**Tier 3** — **Large spills:** these are major incidents that cannot be dealt with effectively under Tier 2 arrangements. They typically occur at sea and cause considerable pollution damage to coastlines over a wide area. A national or international response and resources are required; these are often subject to government controls or direction.

■ The tiered approach to oil spills enables a flexible build up of resources at local, district and national/international levels, as required. Inevitably, in actual incidents the boundaries between tiers may be blurred

Most oil spills are small and can be dealt with locally (Tier 1). An enhanced but compatible response is only required if the incident proves to be beyond the local capability or affects a larger area (Tier 2). To deal with a larger incident, these local plans may form part of a national plan or may be integrated into regional response arrangements covering two or more countries (Tier 3).

Contingency plans should follow a similar layout irrespective of whether they are local, national or regional in scope, although their length and content will vary with the size of the area covered and the degree of risk. Adopting a common format will enable the plans to be compatible and easily understood, while ensuring a smooth transition from one level to the next.

## 11.2 Content of Contingency Plans

Compiling a contingency plan is generally a four-stage process:

- Risk assessment – determining the risks of spills and expected consequences

- strategic policy – defining the roles and responsibilities and providing a summary of the rationale for operations

- operational procedures – establishing procedures for when a spill occurs

- Information Directory – collating supporting data.

The order in which the plan is developed follows this logical progression through the stages. The result of the risk assessment will assist in determining the response strategy, which in turn will assist in developing operational procedures to be followed when a spill occurs. The type of information required in the directory will become clear as these procedures are developed. The steps required to produce a comprehensive contingency plan are set out in Figure 11.1.

### 11.2.1 Risk Assessment

The expected frequency and size of spills, and the types of oil likely to be involved, should be addressed here. Historical spill records may be helpful but, because spills occur infrequently, there is often insufficient data to make a fully quantitative assessment. If such records are unavailable it is usually possible to make comparisons with other locations where they do exist, taking into account variations in circumstances.

For oil terminals and commercial ports, the number of visits made by tankers and other vessels is relevant when assessing risk as small spills often occur as a result of routine operations, such as loading, discharging and bunkering.

A range of possible spill scenarios can be developed from an analysis of oil related activities and the types of oil handled in the area. A note of the physical properties of the oils, particularly the specific gravity, viscosity, pour point at usual sea temperatures and distillation characteristics, may be listed in the Information Directory.

Knowledge of the tides, currents, and the wind speed and direction will help with the prediction of the movement of oil. Reference could also be made to models designed for this purpose. Information on tidal streams or currents should be included in the Information Directory.

Amenity areas, ecologically sensitive areas, industrial sea water intakes, fisheries, mariculture, seabirds, marine mammals and other resources potentially at risk from an oil spill need to be identified. A summary of the important features should be included in this section, while sensitivity maps with detailed information on the location of each resource should be placed in the Information Directory.

### 11.2.2 Strategic Policy

The response strategy should take into account existing civil emergency arrangements as well as cooperation arrangements that may exist between countries in the event that floating oil crosses national borders.

## Risk Assessment

### Determine the likelihood of a spill occurring

- Number and type of vessel calls or vessels passing
- Type and volume of oil carried
- Expected frequency and size of spills
- Identify areas with a high risk of spills

### Determine the probable consequences

- Location of sensitive resources
- Probable spill movement
- Effects of oil on resources

### Determine likely spill scenarios

### Gauge the benefits of developing a contingency plan

- Determine existing spill response arrangements
- Determine whether the proposed contingency arrangements serve to reduce the consequences of a spill
- Decide to what extent a contingency plan is required

## Strategic Policy

### Plan overview

- Identify the lead organisations
- Outline the regulatory framework and jurisdiction
- Define the geographical area of the plan
- Define the interaction with other plans – scaling of tiered response
- Outline the role of the shipowner

### Priorities for protection

- Determine the importance of and ability to protect sensitive resources identified in the risk assessment, accounting for seasonal variation

### Response techniques

- State the preferred response techniques to address floating oil and any restrictions on their use
- Determine the appropriate clean-up techniques for the shoreline types within the plan area
- Outline response to oiled wildlife

### Response resources

- Ensure suitable resources are available to address the risk, either purchased or contracted-in
- Allocate stockpile locations
- Identify suppliers of materials and services likely to be required
- Determine preferred waste storage, treatment and disposal options

### Leadership, command and management

- Define the key response functions
- Outline the divisions of responsibility
- Ensure coordination of all the organisations involved
- Define the responsibility for decisions
- Decide command centre and forward operational base locations
- Outline the involvement of third parties in the response
- Allow for media and public relations

### Training & review procedures

- Outline timetable for training and exercises
- Define the procedure for regular review and update of the plan

## Operational Procedures

### Notification

- Establish notification routes
- Outline the details needed to determine the incident circumstances

### Evaluation

- Source details of the oil, wind & currents – slick trajectory modelling
- Establish the threat to resources
- Obtain additional information from aerial, boat and foot surveys

### Initiation

- Initiate the response
- Identify response team members, their responsibilities and contact details
- Notify or liaise with other organisations, including other plan holders
- Make the response decisions required in the light of threats

### Mobilisation

- Determine availability of resources and outline mobilisation procedures
- Ensure resources are deployed in accordance with strategic policy
- Maintain activity and cost records

### Clean-up support

- Ensure sufficient logistic support
- Ensure integrated communications for all parts of the response
- Determine optimum waste treatment routes

### Progress review

- Ensure all aspects of the response are continuously re-evaluated
- Highlight response aspects requiring modification-scale up or down

### Termination

- Determine the criteria for termination and signing-off work sites
- Demobilise, clean, repair and repatriate resources
- Restore temporary waste sites

### Plan review

Establish a review of the response

## Information Directory

### Operational references

- Contact details and remit of relevant government agencies and other response organisations
- Inventory of available resources and contact details of operators
- Contact details of third party
- Suppliers of materials and services
- Sensitive area maps
- Restrictions on dispersant use

### Sample documents

- Example equipment charter and hire agreements
- Sample pro forma daily aerial, at-sea and shoreline progress reports
- Example forms for recording expenditure

### Supplementary information

- List of approved response products
- Guidelines for observation and recording oil at-sea and on shore
- Guidelines for use of preferred response techniques, including booming plans
- Guidelines for sampling and for monitoring contamination levels
- Sources of funding and compensation
- Information necessary to expedite cost recovery
- Legislation stating statutory powers of the plan holder

■ Figure 11.1: Example of the four stage components required for a comprehensive and well defined contingency plan

## Plan overview

### Shipowner versus government led response

Who it is that meets the immediate costs of a response depends on the arrangements and regulations in the country affected but, generally, two broad approaches are followed: Either the shipowner and their insurers organise the response and meet the immediate costs (shipowner led response) under the direction of a government agency or agencies, or the government undertakes the clean-up (government led response) and claims reimbursement of the costs incurred from the shipowner and their insurers. For a government, a shipowner led response has the benefit that government costs are minimised while the advantage to the shipowner may be that they are in a position to control activities and thereby the costs to a greater extent. However, since shipowners trade globally they require the ability to respond to spills wherever a shipowner led regime is in place and it is clearly very difficult to have a detailed understanding of both the infrastructure and the environmental and commercial sensitivities in all such countries. Many governments resolve this problem, to some extent, by requiring that ships entering their ports contract with a local response organisation.

Other governments take the view that the responsibility for setting priorities for the protection of public resources falls to government and that this is most effectively discharged by government led response. Additionally, if vessels are not routinely destined for ports in a coastal state, the 'passing ship' scenario, the shipowner is unlikely to have a presence in that country and may not readily have the resources to respond to a spill. Because such events are relatively rare, both shipowners and governments find it hard to maintain the necessary expertise and trained spill response personnel. For example, very few contractors are able survive on oil spill work alone and will diversify into other work areas to remain viable. The ability to drop those other contracts and scale up their spill response team at very short notice may present some companies with insurmountable difficulties.

Shipowner led responses are often required in countries that are net importers, particularly of oil cargoes, so that typically most voyages terminate in the ports of such countries. Where a shipowner led response is required, it is essential that the associated regulations are widely promulgated to ensure that shipowners are fully aware of, and able to meet, government expectations should a spill occur. Nevertheless, such arrangements do not diminish the need for well exercised government contingency plans, which should include details of the interface between government and shipowner response organisations.

In the plan overview, the authority or lead agency responsible for the formulation and implementation of the plan and an explanation of the statutory requirements, if any, should be defined. The geographical coverage of the plan should be outlined and reference made to any other related plans. The plan should address how the shipowner's and/or oil industry's contribution to the response would be integrated into government organisational structures.

### Priorities for protection

**Determining priorities for protection is important as, in the event of a major spill, it is unlikely that all resources at risk can be defended successfully.**

Generally, only governmental authorities are in a position to make the required assessment of the economic and environmental importance of a resource to the community. It is essential to take into account not only how desirable the protection of a particular resource would be, but also the extent to which its defence is practical. Provision should also be made for response priorities to be altered if resources are impacted by a spill before the plan can be implemented.

■ **Biologically sensitive areas, such as turtle nesting sites, should be highlighted in a contingency plan**

Seasonal variations can greatly alter priorities. For example, the high priority given to an amenity beach in summer may not apply in winter. Similarly, certain biologically sensitive areas may be assigned a high priority during breeding seasons or when migratory species are known to be present. Sensitivity maps should be clearly annotated with such information.

### Response techniques

Clean-up strategies should be determined in relation to the perceived risk and agreed response priorities. Account should be taken of the limitations of spill control techniques and the most appropriate equipment chosen for the anticipated weather conditions and oil types. For example, boom deployment sites should only be designated where containment and recovery of oil, or its deflection to less sensitive areas, is actually feasible. The different shoreline types falling within the area covered by the plan should be identified and the most appropriate clean-up strategy for each considered. Factors to be taken into account include its amenity value, whether the beaches are easily accessible for heavy equipment and the ability of the shoreline to support such vehicles. Maps and photographs of shoreline types, showing the areas where each technique should be used and where any restrictions might apply, can be included in the Information Directory.

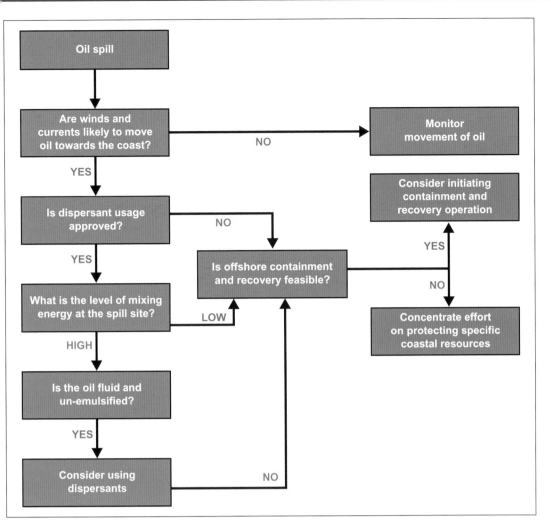

■ **Figure 11.2: A schematic representation of the factors to be considered when selecting clean-up strategies**

A provision for dealing with oiled wildlife, particularly birds, needs to be considered and a response policy decided. Plans should include contact details of vets and specialist care organisations and, at a local level, should also identify existing treatment centres or potential locations for establishing temporary centres.

### Response resources
Keeping equipment close to high risk areas ensures a rapid and effective response. A balance must be found between stockpiling at central points, with the inherent transport costs and delays, and the more expensive option of having equipment packages at every potentially vulnerable site.

Spill response decision tools, such as Figure 11.2, can be of assistance, but there is a danger of over-simplification. In reality, additional factors may have to be taken into account and each case should be judged along with the specific conditions and their relative importance at the time of an incident.

Procedures for mobilisation must be set out in the operational plan, with an inventory of available equipment included in the Information Directory. Descriptions are better presented as a table where details such as type, dimensions, capacity, transport requirements and a contact point for its release are listed against location.

A description of the suitability of equipment, with different types of oils, current velocities, shoreline types etc, will allow for rapid selection of the appropriate equipment. Potential suppliers of non-specialised equipment, such as construction and agricultural machinery, should also be identified.

■ **Procedures for mobilising manpower and resources to remote locations should be outlined in the contingency plan**

In some cases equipment and services will be owned or provided by contractors, industry or other parties and it is useful to define the contractual terms acceptable in principle to the parties concerned in the Information Directory.

The labour required to deploy the equipment and undertake the clean-up will need to be estimated. The extent to which the requirement can be met from the organisation implementing the plan will depend upon availability, the techniques involved and the amount of specialised equipment to be deployed.

■ **The provision of PPE for the workforce should be considered during the planning process**

In the case of large spills, additional manpower may be required, particularly for labour intensive operations such as shoreline clean-up. Sources of backup labour, such as contractors and government departments, should be listed in the Information Directory.

Logistic support is another important element in a contingency plan to ensure that the clean-up operation runs smoothly. Arrangements for providing food, personal protective equipment (PPE), shelter and medical support to clean-up crews must be considered in advance. The availability of backup resources, such as additional equipment, materials and transport, should also be examined, together with the names and addresses of potential suppliers, both within the country and from neighbouring countries.

> **Attention must be given at the planning stage to immigration and customs clearance procedures. Delays may result from normal immigration and customs formalities and the plan should provide for urgent clearance in an emergency, when personnel and equipment need to be brought into a country.**

Temporary storage sites and disposal routes for oily wastes must be agreed in advance. Locations close to areas of greater risk, that are suitable for temporary storage of oil and oily waste, have to be identified. The options for dealing with oily waste should be discussed and a decision made that takes into account the legal requirements, the environmental benefits and the probable costs of each method. Details of the options available should be included in the Information Directory. Temporary storage sites should be shown on the maps describing the shoreline clean-up techniques to be considered in different areas.

## Leadership, command and management

The outline of the response organisation and the responsibilities of those likely to be involved should be described. Responsibility for oil spill control at sea usually rests with a government agency involved in maritime affairs, such as the coast guard or navy. Only rarely, however, do the responsibilities of such agencies extend to the shoreline. Generally, the task of cleaning inshore waters and shorelines falls to port authorities or the local government.

Central coordination by an individual or single organisation that has complete responsibility for handling the operation has advantages and should be considered in order to minimise any confusion that may be caused by divisions of responsibility. Where central coordination under a single organisation is not possible, coordination procedures between the various groups involved in the response need to be agreed.

In a major spill, the on-scene coordinator will delegate control of operations, while for a smaller incident coordination and control functions may be combined.

The size of the organisation depends on the area covered by the plan, the severity of the threat and the sensitivity of the resources at risk. The clean-up of shorelines involves more interests and typically demands greater coordination than the response at sea. In every case, responsibilities should be clearly defined and, as far as possible, the number of authorities involved kept to a minimum.

> ### Incident Command System (ICS)
>
> ICS is a system favoured in the United States and other countries for managing the response to an emergency such as an oil spill. This system brings together a set of policies, procedures, personnel, facilities and equipment into a common framework, within which people from multiple agencies can work together. ICS is a flexible and scalable system that can be expanded or reduced depending on the complexity and demands of any single incident. Because of its widespread application to emergency situations, the many emergency organisations involved in an oil spill should be familiar with its structure and procedures.

The establishment of a fully equipped command post to serve as the focal point for the management of the response and for liaison with outside interests should be predetermined. The centre should act as a central channel for all information and supplies such as charts, maps, reports, manuals etc. In a major spill, operations at sea, on the shore and in the air will be taking place at the same time. In addition to a common radio frequency, it may be necessary to allocate separate frequencies for each operation. Where clean-up operations are conducted over extended distances, portable communications centres may be located close to the scene of each operation.

Liaison arrangements with other interested parties, such as government authorities, salvors and organisations not immediately involved in the response operation but with interests in certain

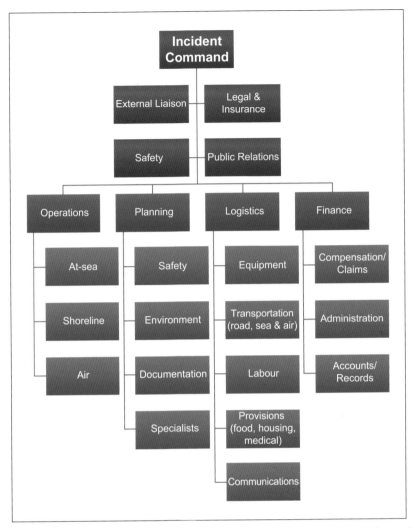

■ **Figure 11.3: Organisational chart for spill response – in the case of minor spills, roles may be combined**

facets of the spill, should be included in the plan. Examples include operators of industrial plants that abstract sea water, environmental protection groups and other government departments. It is often useful to set up a committee to keep all such parties up to date with contingency planning and for consultation during a major spill.

Documentation of actions is important and accurate records should be kept of the use of labour, equipment, materials and expenditure. For the sake of consistency it is helpful to prepare examples of record forms and include them in the Information Directory. Good documentation will assist in formulating claims and cost recovery when the operation is completed.

Provision should be made for keeping the media informed during a spill without interfering with the conduct of the operation. This is likely to require additional telephone lines, media briefing areas and well informed dedicated press officers. For a major spill, consideration should be given to establishing a dedicated website where regular bulletins can be posted, allowing accurate information to be made available within minutes of developments occurring. The various social media services available should also be considered.

## Training and review procedures

Procedures for training and exercises and for updating the plan should be defined. Training should cover a range of subjects, such as response strategies and roles and responsibilities, as well as 'hands on' deployment and operation of equipment and techniques for shoreline clean-up. It is vital that all staff with an identified role in the response are given effective training, from senior managers

■ Regular exercises or drills will ensure that all those likely to be involved in a spill become fully familiar with their particular responsibilities and that contingency arrangements function properly

121

■ **A variety of training methods, both practical and theoretical, can be used**

and administrators through to the on-scene commanders, supervisors and clean-up crews. It should, ideally, consist of a balanced mix of theory and practice. At their simplest level they can take the form of notification exercises, which test alerting and call out procedures, or tabletop exercises that simulate a response situation but do not involve the mobilisation of personnel or equipment. Equipment deployment exercises test the capability of a local team to respond to particular spill scenarios. It is important that providers of boats, trucks etc, and other parties that would normally be part of the response, are involved so that their availability and performance can also be tested. Spill scenarios reflecting an incident of significance affecting wider areas call for the involvement of a range of different organisations and agencies, possibly in various locations. Exercises are designed to expose any weaknesses in the contingency plans, such as delays in the arrangements for equipment deployment. They also allow the timescales required to implement instructions to be realistically assessed and so are good training opportunities.

 An oil spill provides the best opportunity for improving a contingency plan. Events should be reviewed soon after the clean-up operation has been terminated and the plan revised on the basis of lessons learnt, when memories are still fresh.

### 11.2.3   Operational Procedures

The operational part of the plan should describe the recommended procedures for responding to a spill. Many events during the response to an oil spill will occur concurrently, but the format of the operational plan should roughly follow the chronological order of:

- Notification
- evaluation
- initiation
- mobilisation
- clean-up support
- progress review
- termination
- plan review.

### Notification

■ **The first reports of an oil spill can come from a variety of sources**

The first information regarding an oil spill may come from a number of sources, including the general public. The police and other emergency services must hold contact details and radio frequencies allowing them to get in touch with the appropriate 24-hour agency, e.g. the coast guard, military, marine or fire services. On receipt of this information, the designated agency should transmit an initial report as soon as possible to all interested parties, in accordance with an agreed alert procedure. The format of the report should be included in the plan and contain the following:

- Date and time of observation specifying local time or GMT
- position – latitude and longitude or stretch of coast
- source and cause of the pollution (e.g. the name and type of vessel involved; collision, grounding, etc)
- estimate of the amount of oil spilt and the likelihood of further spillage
- description of any oil slicks, including information on direction, length, breadth and appearance
- type of oil spilt and its characteristics
- actions taken or planned to combat pollution and prevent further spillage
- name, occupation and contact details of initial observer and any intermediate reporter.

For the sake of a quick response an initial report should be issued as soon as information relating to at least the first two headings is known, with the remainder transmitted as soon as it is available.

### Evaluation

The plan should include a checklist to assist the on-scene coordinator or duty staff member to evaluate the situation, and to assess the threat posed by the oil. On receipt of the first notification, the coordinator should:

- Determine the expected trajectory of the oil slick at regular intervals
- consider arranging aerial surveillance to verify predictions and obtain further details

- establish surveys of the affected area to verify the reports, e.g. by vessel for floating oil or by foot if the oil has already stranded onshore

- identify threatened resources

- inform the parties who might be affected by the spill.

The data required to make the necessary evaluation, and the sources from where this information is likely to be obtained, should be detailed in the plan as follows:

**Spill details:** the location and type of incident, estimate of the size of the first spill and likelihood of a further spill.
*Source:* Master, vessel or installation operator, salvor, port authority.

**Type of oil:** specific gravity, viscosity, pour point, wax content and distillation characteristics.
*Source:* Master, vessel or installation operator, cargo owner, insurer.

**Natural conditions:** actual and forecast currents, tides and wind.
*Source:* within the Information Directory, local meteorological office tide tables, local charts, websites.

**Sensitivities:** location of vulnerable resources and the priorities for their protection.
*Source:* maps and accompanying notes in the Information Directory, explanations in strategy section.

### Initiation

■ **Planning the response**

If the scale of the initial incident and the threat posed by any spilt oil are considered to be serious, the members of the response team identified in the plan should be notified and a command centre established. An organisation chart of response personnel and a list of their responsibilities, as well as a list of actions to be taken in the first few hours after the incident, will help to expedite the process. To assist with operations, additional responders may be required from outside of the immediate area and contact details of accommodation and catering facilities should be included in the Information Directory. A list of other persons and agencies to be notified according to the severity of the spill should be included, together with a short description of their remit and contact details in the Information Directory.

The plan should list the various response options to be considered:

- If no key resources are threatened, no response may be necessary beyond monitoring the movement and behaviour of the slick

- if key resources are threatened there are two options; combating the oil at a distance or using booms or other measures to defend specific sites

- if no protection is feasible or if resources have already been affected, the priorities for clean-up must be confirmed

- the equipment and labour required must be assessed, together with their availability and location.

**Arrangements should be included in the plan for placing labour and equipment on standby. Equipment may be loaded onto vehicles ready for dispatch and paperwork completed before the actual mobilisation order is given.**

### Mobilisation

■ **Mobilising the military for the clean-up**

Procedures should be laid down for:

- Mobilising the necessary equipment and the labour required to use it

- deploying equipment at sea and on shore, in accordance with the response decision, and placing booms at pre-designated sites to protect key resources, referring to details of mooring points and configurations

- ensuring accurate records are maintained on a daily basis, for each clean-up location, of all the actions taken, labour and equipment deployed and the amounts of materials used.

### Clean-up support
The plan should include procedures for:

- Organising sufficient logistic support so that there are no bottlenecks, (e.g. between oil collection, temporary storage and final disposal) and arranging for the supply of necessary resources

- using aircraft to control clean-up operations at sea and to maintain overall surveillance of the spill, both at sea and on shore

- selecting the most suitable route for the treatment or disposal of wastes, depending on the nature of any oil collected and oily debris

- establishing integrated communications across the response operation (e.g. exchanging mobile phone numbers), specifying radio equipment and frequencies to be used and the allocation of equipment.

**Progress review**
The plan should incorporate procedures for monitoring the progress of the clean-up operation using inputs from aerial surveillance and personnel on site, so that response decisions can be reassessed.

**Termination**
While it is important to end an operation when it becomes ineffective or when the desired level of clean-up has been achieved, it is difficult to give precise guidance on when this might be in a contingency plan. However, provision should be made for:

- Liaison and agreement between all interested parties, at the outset of the operation, regarding the conduct of the operation and the level of clean-up appropriate to each location (i.e. clean-up termination criteria)

- arrangements for joint surveys to be undertaken to decide when end points have been reached

- standing down equipment and returning it to stores for cleaning and maintenance

- re-ordering consumed materials and repairing or replacing damaged equipment

- restoring temporary waste storage sites and cleaning up other work areas.

**Plan review**
Once the response is finalised, a detailed report on the operation should be prepared to support any claims for clean-up expenses and to review the contingency plan.

### 11.2.4  Information Directory

Listings of information that will be required to facilitate an efficient and effective response should be included in this section of the plan. Relevant information includes:

**Contact directory of response personnel:** including all relevant government agencies, local authorities and marine agencies. Out of office contact details should be included where appropriate.

**Contact directory of third parties:** e.g. police, media, parties likely to be affected and other authorities or sources of technical expertise and advice on spill response, safety, environmental and scientific issues.

**Primary response equipment:** government, private contractor and oil industry equipment.

**Auxiliary response equipment:** sources of workboats, tugs, helicopters, aircraft, barges,

vacuum trucks, tractors, protective clothing, hand tools, radios etc.

**Logistics suppliers:** suppliers of catering, housing, transport, sanitation, laundry etc.

■ **Provision of food for the workforce needs to be planned**

**Labour sources:** contractors, local authorities, military, fire brigades, volunteer organisations and other sources.

**Disposal option:** storage and disposal routes for oil and other wastes.

**Oil characteristics:** properties, persistence, likely fate and effects, suitable response techniques etc.

**Currents, tidal ranges, prevailing winds**

**Information on the coastal region:** priorities for protection, strategies and restrictions, dispersant use areas, access points, waste sites etc.

**Information on sensitive areas:** location of amenity and ecologically important areas, sea water intakes, fisheries, mariculture, seabirds and marine mammals and other resources likely to be threatened. Seasonal sensitivity should be highlighted.

The Information Directory might also contain sample documents, such as equipment hire and charter agreements, *pro formas* for recording observations of oiling and the progress of the clean-up and example forms for recording expenditure. Annexes listing, among other things, products approved by an Administration (e.g. dispersants or cleaning agents), relevant legislation and sources of funding and compensation, might also be useful.

Much of the information in the directory is best portrayed through maps, often produced using Geographic Information Systems (GIS) (Figure 11.4).

The scale of the maps and the number required will depend upon the size of the area covered by the contingency plan and the complexity of the features to be illustrated. Those accompanying district and national plans will usually only give a broad indication of the main features of the coastal region, the resources at risk and potential sources of spills. Those accompanying local contingency plans for a restricted length of coastline will provide more detailed information, such as the probable movement of surface slicks, agreed response strategies, shore access points and temporary storage and disposal sites. For clarity, it may be appropriate to divide information between one or more maps. Reference may also be given to additional sketches or photographs that illustrate elements of the response arrangements in more detail (Figure 11.5). Maps should not be regarded as a substitute for written text or for surveys on foot during an incident, but as a means of illustrating key points.

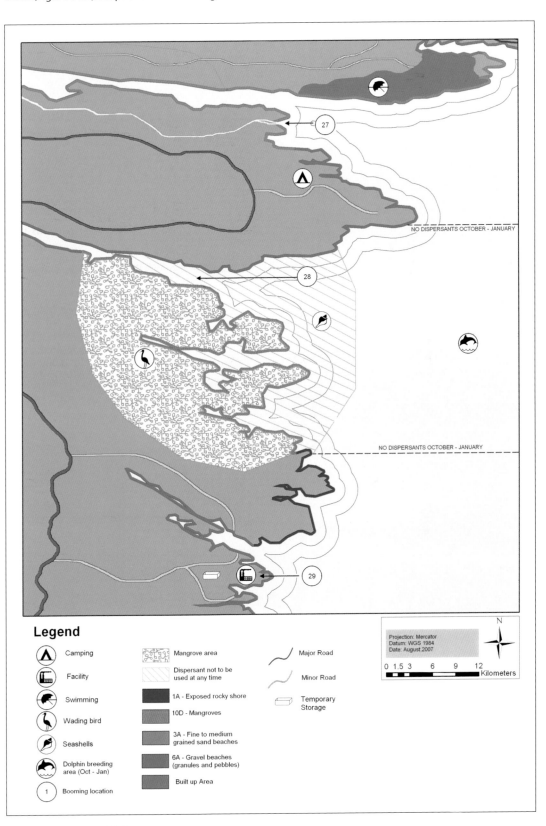

**Legend**

| | | | | | | |
|---|---|---|---|---|---|---|
| Camping | | Mangrove area | | Major Road | | |
| Facility | | Dispersant not to be used at any time | | Minor Road | | |
| Swimming | | 1A - Exposed rocky shore | | Temporary Storage | | |
| Wading bird | | 10D - Mangroves | | | | |
| Seashells | | 3A - Fine to medium grained sand beaches | | | | |
| Dolphin breeding area (Oct - Jan) | | 6A - Gravel beaches (granules and pebbles) | | | | |
| Booming location | | Built up Area | | | | |

Projection: Mercator
Datum: WGS 1984
Date: August 2007

0  1.5  3      6      9      12
Kilometers

NO DISPERSANTS OCTOBER - JANUARY

■ **Figure 11.4: A sensitivity map**

Bathing beach adjacent to hotels and apartment blocks. In the event of pollution, the beach will require priority attention, particularly during the summer months. Good access for vehicles

Boom deployment site near the river mouth. The boom is set to deflect oil to a collection point with good access on the bank.

Tidal flat backed by mangroves and wetlands forming a nature reserve for bird life. While the use of dispersants may be considered for oil approaching this area, consideration should be given to spawning in near shore waters, which may limit its use at certain times of year. The soft mud may not support vehicles and clean-up equipment. Mangroves are sensitive to physical damage.

Power station with a water intake in the foreground. Several deflection booms are deployed to prevent the ingress of oil from a spill.

■ **Figure 11.5: Photographs corresponding to priority areas for spill response on the sensitivity map, Figure 11.4**

## Ten questions for assessing the adequacy of a contingency plan

1. Has there been a realistic assessment of the nature and size of the possible threat, and of the resources most at risk (bearing in mind the probable movement of any oil spilt)?

2. Have priorities for protection been agreed, taking into account the viability of the various protection and clean-up options?

3. Has a strategy for protecting and cleaning the various areas been agreed and clearly explained?

4. Has the organisational structure been outlined and the responsibilities of all those involved been clearly stated with no 'grey areas' - will all who have a task to perform be aware of what is expected of them?

5. Are the levels of equipment, materials and labour sufficient to deal with the anticipated size of spill? If not, have back-up resources been identified and, where necessary, have mechanisms for obtaining their release and entry to the country been established?

6. Have temporary waste storage sites and final disposal routes for oil and debris collected been identified?

7. Are the alerting and initial evaluation procedures fully explained as well as arrangements made for the continual review of the progress and effectiveness of the clean-up operation?

8. Have the arrangements for ensuring effective communication between shore, sea and air been described?

9. Have all aspects of the plan been tested and nothing significant found lacking?

10. Is the plan compatible with plans for adjacent areas and other activities?

# ALTERNATIVE TECHNIQUES 12

The use of booms and skimmers to recover floating oil, and the application of dispersants to enhance natural dispersion, are well established methods of responding to oil spills at sea. However, a number of techniques have been promoted over the years as alternative, or complementary, measures for response to spills at sea and for shoreline clean-up. These include *in-situ* burning and bioremediation.

> When planning to use an alternative response technique, for which responders may have less experience, it is particularly important that prior consideration is given to all aspects of the response, including the requirement for permissions, availability of specialist equipment and the necessary logistical support.

## 12.1 *In-situ* Burning

*In-situ* burning is the term commonly used to describe the controlled burning of oil slicks on the sea surface, often at or near the spill source. *In-situ* burning has the potential to rapidly remove large volumes of oil from the sea surface which, in turn, reduces the volume of oil requiring disposal. Although burning the oil may appear to be a relatively simple operation, in practice there are a number of operational constraints that limit the feasibility of this response method and, as a result, it has rarely been used in actual oil spill cases. The DEEPWATER HORIZON incident, in the Gulf of Mexico in 2010, is a notable exception that has recently revived interest in burning as a viable response option.

■ A burn trial: Burning of oil produces large clouds of smoke that can extend for great distances

### 12.1.1 Feasibility of Burning

Concerns about atmospheric emissions, the potential impact on public health and the limited availability of trained personnel and specialist equipment are some of the reasons why *in-situ* burning has not become a mainstream response option. The smoke plume generated during the burning process is comprised primarily of small carbon particles and combustion gases. Smoke particles are very small fragments of unburnt carbon, which can cause severe health problems if inhaled in high concentrations. From a human health perspective, particles that are small enough to be inhaled into the lungs (particles of less than 10 microns in diameter) pose the greatest concern. The effects on human health will depend on the amount of burn products inhaled and the length of exposure, both of which are related not only to the proximity of the burn to populated areas, but also to the volume of oil burned, burn efficiency and duration and wind speed and direction.

> The proximity of the burn site to populated areas is one of the key considerations when deciding whether *in-situ* burning should be included in the response to an oil spill.

Following an accidental fire on board the CASTILLO DE BELLVER (South Africa, 1983), clouds of black smoke resulted in an oily rain falling on farms up to 80 km inland, contaminating sheep and wheat. Fortunately, most of this residue was subsequently washed away. The accidental ignition of the cargo on board the AEGEAN SEA (Spain, 1992) caused dense clouds of black smoke to threaten the town of La Coruña, leading to temporary mass evacuation. In addition, black soot coated several buildings, which required cleaning. Although both incidents are not examples of intentional *in-situ* burning, they illustrate the possible consequences of burning oil when the smoke could be carried across inhabited areas.

As with dispersant use, there is a 'window of opportunity' for *in-situ* burning. An understanding of the fate and behaviour of the oil is important when considering whether this technique will be effective because, as time progresses, fuel and crude oils become increasingly difficult to ignite. As the lighter, more volatile, components of the oil are lost through evaporation, the rate at which the flames spread across the surface of the slick decreases. The formation of oil-in-water emulsions can also prevent the slick from being ignited successfully. Furthermore, fragmentation and scattering of the slick over a wide area by winds and currents reduces the operational efficiency of *in-situ* burning. Due to the negative impacts these weathering processes have on *in-situ* burning, it is important that decision-making and resource mobilisation occur in a timely manner.

**DEEPWATER HORIZON – Gulf of Mexico, 2010**

The offshore drilling rig, DEEPWATER HORIZON, working approximately 40 miles off the south-east coast of Louisiana in the Gulf of Mexico, suffered an explosion in April 2010 and subsequently sank. During June and July a number of efforts were made, using various containment systems, to stem the flow of oil from the well. The well was capped on 15 July and, in early August, cementing operations (as part of a procedure called 'static kill') plugged the leak. The well was finally sealed in September, having released an estimated 4.9 million barrels (approximately 668,360 tonnes) of oil into the marine environment.

In conjunction with containment and recovery operations and chemical dispersion, *in-situ* burning was used in an effort to minimise impacts to the shoreline and sensitive resources. More than 400 burns were conducted, which are estimated to have eliminated around 30,000 to 50,000 tonnes of oil, accounting for approximately 5% of the total volume spilt. Due to the unique circumstances of the DEEPWATER HORIZON incident, burning was one of the primary response options rather than an 'alternative technique'. A number of factors contributed to the successful use of burning in this case; primarily the distance from the shoreline, which reduced concern about the potential impact on public health of harmful or prolonged smoke exposure, and the continuous supply of fresh oil from the well head, which extended the 'window of opportunity' to use the technique.

The authorities consistently monitored air quality and any emissions from the burning oil. Scientists at the National Oceanic and Atmospheric Administration (NOAA) subsequently investigated the atmospheric damage that the burning operation may have caused. In a study published by the NOAA and its Cooperative Institute for Research in Environmental Sciences, it was reported that around 0.63 to 2.07 million kilograms of black carbon or soot were pumped into the atmosphere over the Gulf of Mexico. The study also found that the hot soot plumes from the burns reached much higher into the atmosphere than ship emissions normally rise to, potentially prolonging the amount of time that the black carbon can remain in the atmosphere and affecting the distance travelled by it. This research will aid future decision-making on the net environmental benefits of burning as a primary response technique.

Image courtesy of USCG

■ **A controlled burn of oil from the DEEPWATER HORIZON oil spill**

### 12.1.2 Operational Issues

To sustain *in-situ* burning, fuel, oxygen and an ignition source will be required. A slick of weathered crude or light fuel oil must have a minimum thickness of 2 to 3 mm (to counter the cooling effect of the sea) and, once the slick has reduced to a thickness of approximately 1 mm, the burn will extinguish naturally. Oil spill containment booms are usually used to increase and maintain the thickness of the slick.

Traditional offshore containment booms can be used to recover and contain the oil at sea and to divert the oil to where the burning will occur. However, the heat generated during burning causes conventional containment booms to burn or melt, leading to escape of the oil. Consequently, to undertake *in-situ* burning effectively a specialist fire boom will be required. Fire booms resist fire damage in one of two ways: some are manufactured using fire resistant materials such as stainless steel or ceramic fibres while others are protected via a water cooling system. Stockpiles of specialist fire booms are quite limited when compared with stockpiles of conventional booms and fire booms tend to be very expensive.

■ *In-situ* **burning using fire booms**

There are several ways of igniting a slick, ranging from specifically developed ignition systems to simple *ad hoc* methods. The various methods fall into two categories: those deployed from the sea surface and those deployed aerially. The most advanced, and generally regarded as the safest ignition device, is the helitorch, which utilises technology originally developed for use in forest fire management. These helicopter-slung devices emit a stream of gelled fuel that ignites as it leaves the unit.

As with any at-sea response, the weather and environmental conditions can impact on the effectiveness and safety of the burning operation. It is generally recognised that strong winds (greater than 10 ms$^{-1}$ or 20 knots) can make it difficult to ignite the oil and, once alight, may extinguish the fire or make it difficult to control. Also, wave heights of more than 1 m can result in oil splashing over the boom. Typically, fire booms are more fragile than conventional booms and are, therefore, more susceptible to damage from excessive winds, waves and currents.

In some areas ice can act as a natural containment mechanism to prevent the spread of oil, which may remove the need for specialist containment booms.

Realistically, *in-situ* burning is most likely to be acceptable in remote or ice covered waters, where there may be less concern about smoke plumes and/or containment.

■ **Burning of oil in ice**

From an operational perspective, even a very efficient burn will not remove all of the oil. Not only will burning produce gases and a large amount of black smoke, it will also leave behind a burn residue. Research has shown that, in general, burn residues contain a greater quantity of heavy components than lighter components and are more viscous than the original oil. Various terms have been used to describe the residues left after burning including: 'tarry lumps', 'brittle solids' and 'semi solid tar-like layers'. The nature of the residue will depend on the oil type, thickness, degree of weathering and efficiency of the burn.

■ **Residue from a burn**

Burning removes the more toxic components of the oil, but the residue has the potential to coat and smother biota and affect birds and mammals that come into contact with it. Therefore, attempts should be made to collect the residue wherever possible. One of the key issues is the potential for some residues to sink. Research has shown that medium and light crude oils, condensates and light and intermediate refined products are more likely to produce burn residues that float, but heavy crude oils and heavy refined products are more likely to produce residues that sink.

Sunken residue may smother or poison bottom dwelling (benthic) species and it is very difficult to recover. It can also contaminate fishing gear or nearby shorelines, especially following storms or changes in the current or tide, as occurred following the explosion and fire on board the BETELGEUSE (Ireland, 1979) and the HAVEN (Italy, 1991). Crude oil was deliberately ignited in the response to an oil spill in South Korea, in 1983, and, as a result,

a dense residue formed that sank and seriously contaminated shellfish beds.

The regulatory permissions required to conduct *in-situ* burning vary from country to country. However, concern over public health and airborne pollution is often a major obstacle to gaining permission to use the technique in an actual spill. For *in-situ* burning to be effective it is important that specialist booms and trained experts are available to respond in a timely manner. Suitable vessels for transporting equipment and towing booms, and surveillance aircraft to support the operation, also need to be available. Given the specialist nature of this technique, the feasibility of using it should be fully considered as part of a contingency plan and, if it is regarded as a possible response option, exercises to test the arrangements should be carried out on a regular basis.

## 12.2 Bioremediation

Biodegradation is the natural process whereby bacteria or other microorganisms alter and break down organic molecules. Oil, like many natural substances, will biodegrade over a period of time into simple compounds such as carbon dioxide, water and biomass. Bioremediation is the term used to describe the addition of materials to contaminated environments, such as oil spill sites, to cause an acceleration of the natural biodegradation process. There are two main strategies for bioremediation: the first is biostimulation, which involves the application of nutrients, and the second is bioaugmentation, which entails the addition of oil degrading microorganisms to supplement existing microbial populations. Bioremediation is a response technique that is used primarily on land rather than at sea. This is because the movement and weathering of the oil and the dilution of the product into the sea make it difficult to keep the product in contact with the oil long enough for biodegradation to be stimulated.

Microorganisms, such as bacteria, fungi, unicellular algae and protozoa, are present everywhere and biodegrade (metabolise) organic components for energy and as a source of carbon for cell growth. The primary processes of microbial degradation require oxygen (aerobic conditions) although in the absence of oxygen (anaerobic conditions) degradation can occur, but at very slow rates. The rate at which degradation occurs is influenced by several factors, the key ones being the levels of microorganisms, nutrients and oxygen present in the immediate environment and the temperature. Salinity and pH also affect the rate at which oil biodegrades in the environment.

### 12.2.1 Biostimulation

To work effectively, microorganisms require sufficient levels of carbon, nitrogen and phosphorus. The relative levels of these three elements is referred to as the C:N:P ratio. When an oil spill occurs, the oil provides a huge amount of carbon, but a lack of additional nitrogen and phosphorous can then limit the growth of microbial populations. Biostimulation, by the application of fertilizers, can adjust the balance in the C:N:P ratio and enhance the degradation rate by the indigenous (i.e. naturally occurring) microbial community. However, the concentrations of nitrogen and phosphorus required to achieve and maintain the optimum C:N:P ratio vary considerably and depend on the oil properties and the environmental conditions.

## 12.2.2 Bioaugmentation

The theory behind bioaugmentation is that microorganisms are applied to contaminated shorelines, (sometimes referred to as 'seeding') to enhance the biodegradation of oil. A number of commercial products are available that contain microorganisms specifically selected for their oil degrading abilities. The process assumes that indigenous microbial populations are not capable of sufficiently degrading the oil and that seeding will reduce the time required. However, oil degrading microorganisms are distributed widely throughout the world's coastal areas and are particularly abundant in coastlines adjacent to chronically polluted waters, such as those that receive industrial discharges and untreated sewage. In these areas the addition of microorganisms will not be necessary. Even in regions where the oil degrading community is less abundant, it is unlikely that bioaugmentation will significantly enhance biodegradation.

One of the concerns about bioaugmentation relates to the potential impact of introducing new species to an area, which is subject to regulation in some countries. However, in most cases it is unlikely that seeded microorganisms will be able to compete successfully with indigenous populations.

Studies have shown that stimulating naturally occurring microorganisms through biostimulation has had a greater effect on the rate of oil biodegradation than the introduction of microorganisms through bioaugmentation.

## 12.2.3 Limitations of Use

Crude oils are made up of a wide spectrum of hydrocarbons ranging from very volatile, light materials such as benzene and toluene to more complex, heavy compounds such as bitumens. Refined products such as petrol or fuel oil are composed of smaller and more specific ranges of these hydrocarbons. The thousands of different compounds are usually categorised into four groups: saturated hydrocarbons, aromatic hydrocarbons, resins and asphaltenes. It is important to remember that different oils have different potentials for biodegradation depending on the proportion of compounds from these four groups. It should be recognised that some of the more complex components of the oil may remain partially or totally un-degraded. For example, resins and asphaltenes biodegrade very slowly, if at all.

**Bioremediation is usually considered as a final polishing technique and is not recommended for removing bulk oil from shorelines, for which there are much more efficient, well established methods of cleaning.**

From an operational perspective, aerobic conditions are considered necessary for efficient bioremediation. Dissolved oxygen is usually available in sufficient quantities in the surface layers of most beach environments because of constant aeration by wave and tide action. However, the availability of oxygen may become a limiting factor in salt marshes, mud flats and fine grain shorelines. As biodegradation only occurs at the oil-water interface, oil that is stranded in thick layers on the shoreline at, or above, the high water mark (where contact with water is restricted) is likely to biodegrade extremely slowly.

Temperature is another factor that affects the rate of biodegradation. It influences the process in two ways; first, on the activity of the microorganisms and second, on the properties of the spilt oil. Research has shown that biodegradation occurs in most sea water temperature ranges, with rates being faster at higher temperatures.

Laboratory and mesocosm studies have shown that bioremediation techniques can increase rates of degradation, and bioremediation is widely practised as a technique for dealing with contaminated soil in land farms, for example. However, laboratories and on-land sites represent closed or semi-enclosed environments where the physical, chemical and biological factors that affect bioremediation can be controlled more easily to provide optimum conditions for biodegradation. Oil spilt at sea typically strands in the intertidal zone, where it is recognised that trying to maintain optimum nutrient concentrations is difficult due to nutrient washout caused by waves and tides.

In principle, bioremediation is considered to be most applicable in sheltered shorelines because the treated sediments are not exposed to significant tidal actions and, therefore, suffer less from nutrient washout. However, oil within sensitive shores, such as salt marshes and mud flats, is generally better left to weather naturally. When deciding whether bioremediation is a suitable technique to assist with removing the oil from these environments, consideration should be given to whether or not the oil has penetrated below the aerobic surface layer, and therefore the likely effectiveness of this technique. Such environments are highly susceptible to trampling and substrate erosion and even very carefully conducted activities may cause more damage than the oil itself. Tilling the substrate to introduce oxygen to a greater depth will almost certainly cause greater harm to these sensitive environments.

## 12.2.4 Considerations for Use

Bioremediation should be considered as a longer term strategy and there should be sufficient time to adequately plan its use. Any bioremediation strategy employed must be specific to the area being treated as the success of any treatment will depend on the properties of the oil, the nature of the bioremediation products and the characteristics of the contaminated area.

To make an informed decision on whether to use bioremediation, relevant information should be gathered and reviewed prior to making an assessment. Key information would include the type of oil spilt, (i.e. the proportion of components that are easily biodegraded) the type of shoreline affected and information on background concentrations of nutrients and the presence of microorganisms.

If a decision is made to use bioremediation, additional information and planning is required before the strategy can be implemented. Careful consideration should be given to the type and quantity of product that will be used, how it will be applied and the frequency of re-applications.

It is important to monitor the overall effectiveness of the bioremediation strategy. Sediment samples can be analysed to establish the degree of biodegradation using gas chromatography with flame ionization detection (GC-FID) or gas chromatography mass spectrometry (GC-MS). Any bioremediation treatment plan should include agreed 'end points' for when the technique will be terminated. As already noted, not all components of oil will biodegrade and, therefore, an appropriate 'end point' should focus on reaching acceptable levels of residual oil and/or habitat recovery.

Biodegradation is a natural process and, given sufficient time, microorganisms are able to degrade many components of oil in the environment. Frequently, the concentration of oil residue remaining after significant biodegradation has taken place, i.e. the 'end point', will be the same whether nutrients or microorganisms are added or not; the difference being that the 'end point' may be reached quicker. However, the timescale for bioremediation is still of the order of months.

■ An area of mangrove set aside for bioremediation following an oil spill in India

While bioremediation has been used successfully to treat contaminated soil *in-situ*, it has not been shown conclusively that it is effective on oiled shorelines. Nevertheless, it is possible that bioremediation may have a role to play in situations where nutrient levels are severely depleted. However, questions concerning the cost effectiveness of this technique, combined with fears of adding yet more nutrients to shore waters where eutrophic conditions are already of concern, renders this technique less viable.

# 12.3 Other Alternative Techniques

In addition to dispersants, a variety of other chemical products have been developed and promoted to assist with cleaning up or removing oil. These include shoreline cleaning agents, herders and solidifiers. Approval must be obtained from the appropriate authorities before applying any chemical agents.

## 12.3.1 Shoreline Cleaning Agents

Shoreline cleaning agents, sometimes called surface washing agents (SWAs), are chemical products designed to aid the removal of oil from hard surfaces. Surface cleaners are different from dispersants in that they are manufactured to help 'lift' the oil from a surface rather than disperse it. However, it is known that some products approved for use as surface cleaners can actually act to disperse the oil.

 **Typically, surface cleaning agents are used to help remove weathered or heavy oil from surfaces where cleaning methods such as flushing or high pressure washing alone are not adequate. They are normally used on surfaces such as quay walls and other manmade structures, as well as on boulders.**

The product is applied at an appropriate dose rate, usually as per the manufacturer's instructions, directly onto the surface and typically using a backpack or hand-held sprayer. The cleaning agent is then left to soak for a specified period of time and may be 'worked in' using a wire or stiff bristled brush. The surface is then cleaned by low pressure flushing, preferably with cold water at moderate pressure. Ideally, the wash water should be contained in order for the oil to be collected using booms, skimmers and/or sorbent material.

■ Cleaning rip-rap with a shoreline cleaning agent

For those products that act to disperse the oil it will not be possible to recover it. When used in intertidal areas, surface cleaners should be applied at or around low tide to allow sufficient time for the product to soak into the oiled substrate.

Before deciding to use surface cleaners over a large area it is recommended that a small trial is conducted as this can help to determine the appropriate soak time and ensure that the product is effective at removing the oil. A number of countries have lists of approved surface cleaners and, in these instances, only approved products should be used.

## 12.3.2  Herders

Herders, or collecting agents, are chemical products designed to overcome some of the limitations associated with traditional recovery techniques by limiting the spread of oil. The efficiency of a skimmer largely depends on whether it is constantly being supplied with a relatively thick layer of oil, but the tendency of oil slicks to spread rapidly in open water makes it difficult to ensure that the skimmer encounters oil at an optimum recovery rate. Early research and field trials focused on investigating whether herders could contain oil in a small area and thereby improve a skimmer's encounter rate. However, studies found that, in all but very calm seas, the chemically herded slick started to spread out soon after application. Although herding agents are not used to aid mechanical recovery at sea, they are sometimes considered for use in sheltered or inaccessible areas, such as under piers. However, where the aim of using herders is to thicken and push oil out of inaccessible areas, it may be just as effective to do this by directing a spray of water towards the oil, creating a current that results in the movement and concentration. Recent research has focused on the potential benefits of using herders to assist *in-situ* burning in ice infested waters, in dispersant spraying operations and on the collection of oil from sensitive areas such as marshes.

## 12.3.3  Solidifiers

Solidifiers, also known as gelling agents, react with oil to form rubber-like solids that can be picked up from the water's surface using nets or suction equipment. They are available in various forms, including dry powder, granules or semi-solid material, and can be contained in booms, pillows, pads and socks. Solidifiers have not gained widespread acceptance for removing oil slicks at sea due, in part, to the large quantities of the material that must be applied. This can be as much as three times the volume of the spill. Furthermore, traditional response equipment, such as skimmers, pumps and tanks, are designed to deal with liquid or viscous oil and will not work if the oil has solidified at sea. Solidifiers are most suitable for small, land-based spills, or spills in confined areas such as harbours.

## General

CEDRE (2007) **Understanding Black Tides (Learning package)**. CEDRE, Brest, France. 118pp.

Clark, R.B. (2001) **Marine Pollution**. 5th edition. Oxford University Press, Oxford, UK. 248pp.

De la Rue, C. & Anderson, C. (2009) **Shipping and the Environment: Law and Practice**. 2nd edition. Informa Law, London, UK. 1247pp.

Fingas, M. (editor) (2011) **Oil Spill Science and Technology: Prevention, Response and Cleanup**. Gulf Professional Publishing Elsevier/1156pp.

Fingas, M.F. (2000) **The Basics of Oil Spill Cleanup**. 2nd edition. CRC Press LLC, Florida, USA. 233pp. *New edition expected 2012.*

Gold, E. (2006) **Gard Handbook on Protection of the Marine Environment**. 3rd edition. Assuranceforeningen Gard, Arendal, Norway. 945pp.

Hooke, N. (1997) **Maritime Casualties 1963-1996**. 2nd edition. LLP, London, UK. 741pp.

IMO (2005) **Manual on Oil Pollution - Section IV. Combating Oil Spills**. International Maritime Organization, IMO, London, UK. 230pp.

## Chapter 1: Sources of Petroleum Hydrocarbons

GESAMP (IMO/FAO/UNESCO-IOC/WMO/UNIDO/IAEA/UN/UNEP Joint Group of Experts on the Scientific Aspects of Marine Pollution) (2007) **Estimates of Oil Entering the Marine Environment from Sea-based Activities**. GESAMP Reports and Studies No. 75. International Maritime Organization, IMO, London, UK. 83pp.

GESAMP (IMO/FAO/UNESCO/WMO/WHO/IEA/UN/UNEP Joint Group of Experts on the Scientific Aspects of Marine Pollution) (1993) **Impact of Oil and Related Chemicals and Wastes on the Marine Environment**. GESAMP Reports and Studies No.50. International Maritime Organization, IMO, London, UK. 180pp.

IMO (2011) **MARPOL Consolidated Edition 2011**. International Maritime Organization, IMO, London, UK.

National Research Council (2003) **Oil in the Sea III. Inputs, Fates and Effects**. National Academies Press, Washington DC, USA. 265pp.

## Chapter 2: Fate of Marine Oil Spills

Davies, J.M., Topping, G. (1997) **The Impact of an Oil Spill in Turbulent Waters: BRAER**. Proceedings of a symposium held at the Royal Society of Edinburgh, 7-8 September 1995. Stationery Office Ltd, Edinburgh, UK. 288pp.

National Research Council (2003) **Oil in the Sea III. Inputs, Fates and Effects**. National Academies Press, Washington DC, USA. 265pp.

## Chapter 3: Aerial Surveillance at Sea

Bonn Agreement (2009) **Bonn Agreement Aerial Operations Handbook, 2009**. Bonn Agreement, London, UK. 60pp.

CEDRE (2004) **Aerial Observation of Oil Pollution at Sea. Operational Guide**. CEDRE, Brest, France. 60pp.

Dicks, B., Moller, T., Santner, R. (1998) **The EVOIKOS and PONTOON 300 Incidents - The Technical Adviser's Perspective**. Proceedings of the Petroleum Association of Japan (PAJ) Oil Spill Symposium 98, 7-8 October 1998, Tokyo, Japan. 13pp.

Sanderson, P.G. (2001) **The Application of Satellite Remote Sensing to Coastal Management in Singapore**. AMBIO: A Journal of the Human Environment 30(1) pp.43-48.

## Chapter 4: Oil on Shorelines

CEDRE (2006) **Surveying Sites Polluted by Oil. Operational Guide**. CEDRE, Brest, France. 54pp.

IMO (1998) **Manual on Oil Pollution - Section VI. Guidelines for Sampling and Identification of Oil Spills.** International Maritime Organization, IMO, London, UK. 38pp.

Sergy, G.A. & Owens, E.H. (2000) **The SCAT manual. A Field Guide to the Documentation and Description of Oiled Shorelines**. Environment Canada, Edmonton, Alberta, Canada. 223pp.

Wang, Z., Stout, S. (2007) **Oil Spill Environmental Forensics: Fingerprinting and Source Identification**. Elsevier Academic Press, Burlington MA, USA. 620pp.

## Chapter 5: Environmental Effects of Oil Spills

CEDRE (2007) **Ecological Monitoring of Accidental Water Pollution. Operational Guide**. CEDRE, Brest, France. 37pp.

EXXON VALDEZ Oil Spill Trustee Council **Status of Restoration: Sea Otters**. www.evostc.state.ak.us/recovery/status_seaotter.cfm (accessed 26/10/10).

Hughes, B., Haycock, B., Musgrove, A.J., Cranswick, P.A., Banks, A.N., Fairney, N.P., Smith, L.E., Sanderson, W.G., Whitehead, S. (2008) **The SEA EMPRESS Oil Spill (Wales, UK): Effects on Common Scoter Melanitta Nigra in Carmarthen Bay and Status Ten Years Later**. Marine Pollution Bulletin, 56 (5) pp.895-902.

IMO/UNEP (2009) **IMO/UNEP Guidance Manual on the Assessment and Restoration of Environmental Damage Following Marine Oil Spills**. International Maritime Organization, IMO, London, UK. 103pp.

IMO (1997) **Field Guide for Oil Spill Response in Tropical Waters**. International Maritime Organization, IMO, London, UK. 54pp.

IPIECA (2000) **Choosing Spill Options to Minimize Damage: Net Environmental Benefit Analysis**. IPIECA Report Series Volume 10. IPIECA, London, UK. 20pp.

IPIECA (1999) **Biological Impacts of Oil Pollution: Sedimentary Shores**. IPIECA Report Series Volume 9. IPIECA, London, UK. 24pp.

IPIECA (1996) **Biological Impacts of Oil Pollution: Rocky Shores**. IPIECA Report Series Volume 7. IPIECA, London, UK. 20pp.

IPIECA (1994) **Biological Impacts of Oil Pollution: Saltmarshes**. IPIECA Report Series Volume 6. IPIECA, London, UK. 20pp.

IPIECA (1992) **Biological Impacts of Oil Pollution: Coral Reefs**. IPIECA Report Series Volume 3. IPIECA, London, UK. 16pp.

IPIECA (1993) **Biological Impacts of Oil Pollution: Mangroves**. IPIECA Report Series Volume 4. IPIECA, London, UK. 20pp.

IPIECA (1991) **Guidelines on Biological Impacts of Oil Pollution**. IPIECA Report Series Volume 1. IPIECA, London, UK. 15pp.

Law, R., Kirby, M.F., Moore, J., Barry, J., Sapp, M. Balaam, J. (2011) **PREMIAM – Pollution Response in Emergencies Marine Impact Assessment and Monitoring: Post-Incident Monitoring Guidelines**. Science Series Technical Report, Cefas, Lowestoft, UK146. 164pp.

Monson, D.H., Doak, D.F., Ballachey, B.E., Johnson, A., Bodkin, J.L. (2000) **Long-Term Impacts of the EXXON VALDEZ Oil Spill on Sea Otters, Assessed Through Age-dependent Mortality Patterns**. Proceedings of the National Academy of Sciences of the United States of America, 97 (12) pp.6562-6567.

Moore, J. (2006) **Long Term Ecological Impacts of Marine Oil Spills (Paper 15)**. Paper presented at INTERSPILL 2006, 21-23 March 2006, ExCel, London, UK. UK Spill Association, Southampton, UK. 14pp.

Owens, E.H., Sergy, G. (2005) **Time Series Observations of Marsh Recovery and Pavement Persistence at Three Metula Spills Sites After 30 1/2 Years**. Proceedings of the twenty-eighth Arctic and marine oilspill program (AMOP) technical seminar, June 7-9 2005, pp.463-472. Environment Canada, Ottawa, Canada.

## Chapter 6: Economic Effects of Oil Spills

CEDRE (2007) **Response to Small-scale Pollution in Ports and Harbours. Operational Guide**. CEDRE, Brest, France. 49pp.

Davies, J.M., Topping, G. (1997) **The Impact of an Oil Spill in Turbulent Waters: BRAER**. Proceedings of a symposium held at the Royal Society of Edinburgh, 7-8 September 1995. Stationery Office Ltd, Edinburgh, UK. 288pp.

IMO (2003) **IMO/FAO Guidance on Managing Seafood Safety During and After Oil Spills**. International Maritime Organization, IMO, London, UK. 21pp.

IOPC Fund 1992 (2008) **Claims Manual International Oil Pollution Compensation Fund 1992**, London, UK 37pp.

IPIECA (1997) **Biological Impacts of Oil Pollution: Fisheries**. IPIECA Report Series Volume 8. IPIECA, London, UK. 28pp.

Moller, T., Dicks, B., Whittle, K.J., Girin, M. (1999) **Fishing and Harvesting Bans in Oil Spill Response**. Proceedings of the International Oil Spill Conference 1999, 7-12 March 1999, Seattle, USA, pp.693-700. American Petroleum Institute, Washington DC, USA.

## Chapter 7: Containment and Recovery

Cabioc'h, F. et al (2005) **ERIKA vs PRESTIGE: Two Similar Accidents, Two Different Responses. The French Case**. Proceedings of the International Oil Spill Conference 2005, May 15-19 2005, Miami Beach, Florida, USA. American Petroleum Institute, Washington DC, USA. 7pp.

Cabioc'h, F., Peigne, G. (2001) **Offshore Operations Following the ERIKA Oil Spill**. Proceedings of the 2001 International Oil Spill Conference, March 26-29 2001, Tampa Convention Center, Tampa, Florida, USA, pp.657-659. American Petroleum Institute, Washington DC, USA.

Morrison, J., Potter, S. (2008) **World Catalog of Oil Spill Response Products 2008**. SL Ross Environmental Research Ltd. Ontario, Canada. ~400pp.

Nichols, J. (1994) **Response to Marine Oil Spills from Tankers - Case Histories**. Paper presented at GAOCMAO/KOC Conference on Tanker Operations and Marine Environment in the Gulf, Kuwait, 25-26th January, 1994. Kuwait Oil Company, (KOC)/GAOCMAO, Kuwait. 18pp.

O'Brien, M. (2002) **At-sea Recovery of Heavy Oils – A Reasonable Response Strategy**? Paper presented at 3rd R&D Forum on High Density Oil Spill Response, 11-13 March 2002, Brest, France. International Maritime Organization, London, UK. 20pp.

## Chapter 8: The Use of Dispersants

CEDRE (2005) **Using Dispersant to Treat Oil Slicks at Sea. Operational Guide**. CEDRE, Brest, France. 54pp.

Chapman, H., Purnell, K., Law, R.J., Kirby, M. (2007) **The Use of Chemical Dispersants to Combat Oil Spills at Sea: A Review of Practice and Research Needs in Europe**. Marine Pollution Bulletin 54 (7) pp.827-838.

EMSA (2010) **Manual on the Applicability of Oil Spill Dispersants**. Version 2. European Maritime Safety Agency, Lisbon, Portugal. 106pp.

Energy Institute (2004) **Operational Guidelines on the Use of Oil Spill Dispersants at Sea**. Energy Institute, London, UK. 37pp.

Holm, E.K. (editor) (2011) **Dispersants in Oil Spills. Issues and Research**. Nova Science Publishers, Inc, New York, USA. 134pp.

IMO/UNEP (1995) IMO/UNEP **Guidelines on Oil Spill Dispersant Application Including Environmental Considerations**. International Maritime Organization, IMO, London, UK. 55pp.

IPIECA (2001) **Dispersants and Their Role in Oil Spill Response**. 2nd edition. IPIECA Report Series Volume 5. IPIECA, London, UK. 36pp.

Lewis, A. (2001) **Oil Spill Dispersants**. SINTEF, Trondheim, Norway. 27pp.

Lunel, T., Rusin, J., Bailey, N., Halliwell, C., Davies, L. (1997) **The net Environmental Benefit of a Successful Dispersant Operation at the SEA EMPRESS Incident**. Proceedings of the 1997 International Oil Spill Conference, Fort Lauderdale, Florida, USA, 7-10 April 1997, pp.185-194. American Petroleum Institute, Washington DC, USA.

National Research Council (2005) **Oil Spill Dispersants Efficacy and Effects**. The National Academies Press, Washington DC, USA. 377pp.

National Research Council (1989) **Using Oil Spill Dispersant on the Sea**. National Academies Press, Washington DC, USA. 335pp.

## Chapter 9: Shoreline Clean-up

CEDRE (2009) **Use of Sorbents for Spill Response. Operational Guide**. CEDRE, Brest, France. 52pp.

Dicks, B., Parker, H., Purnell, K., Santner, R. (2002) **Termination of Shoreline Cleanup – a Technical Perspective**. Paper presented at CEDRE seminar "Technical Lessons Learnt from the ERIKA Incident and Other Spills", 13-15 March 2002, Brest, France. 12pp.

Dicks, B., Parker, H., Moller, T., Purnell, K., White, I. (2000) **Management and Work Force Requirements for Effective Shoreline Cleaning Operations**. Paper presented at INTERSPILL 2000, A New Millennium - A New Approach to Spill Response, International Conference and Exhibition, 28-30 November 2000, Brighton, UK. 14pp.

IPIECA (2002) **Oil Spill Responder Safety Guide**. IPIECA Report Series Volume 11. IPIECA, London, UK. 32pp.

Purnell, K. (2002) **Recent Activities of ITOPF, the AMORGOS Incident and Considerations of NEBA**. Paper presented at Petroleum Association of Japan (PAJ) Oil Spill Symposium 2002, 6-7 March, Tokyo, Japan. 10pp.

## Chapter 10: Disposal of Oil and Oiled Material

CEDRE (2007) **Oil Spill Waste Management. Operational Guide**. CEDRE, Brest, France. 59pp.

Colcombe, K., Bedborough, D. (1997) **Shoreline Cleanup and Waste Disposal Issues During the SEA EMPRESS Incident**. Proceedings of the 1997 International Oil Spill Conference, Fort Lauderdale, Florida, USA, 7-10 April 1997, pp.195-203. American Petroleum Institute, Washington DC, USA.

IPIECA (2004) **Guidelines for Oil Spill Waste Minimization and Management**. IPIECA Report Series Volume 12. IPIECA, London, UK. 19pp.

Scherrer, P., Couvreur, J.-F. (2001) **Treatment of Waste from the ERIKA Spill**. Proceedings of the 2001 International Oil Spill Conference, March 26-29 2001, Tampa Convention Center, Tampa, Florida, USA, pp.745-749. American Petroleum Institute, Washington DC, USA.

## Chapter 11: Contingency Planning

IMO (2010) **Manual on Oil Spill Risk Evaluation and Assessment of Response Preparedness**. International Maritime Organization, IMO, London, UK. 54pp.

IMO (2010) **Guidelines for the Development of Shipboard Marine Pollution Emergency Plans**. International Maritime Organization, IMO, London, UK. 61pp.

IMO (2009) **Manual on Oil Pollution - Section V. Administrative Aspects of Oil Pollution Response**. International Maritime Organization, IMO, London, UK. 99pp.

IMO (1995) **Manual on Oil Pollution - Section II. Contingency Planning**. International Maritime Organization, IMO, London, UK. 65pp.

IMO/IPIECA (1996) **Sensitivity Mapping for Oil Spill Response**. IMO/IPIECA Report Series Volume 1. IPIECA, London, UK. 24pp.

IMO/IPIECA (1996) **Guide to Oil Spill Exercise Planning**. IMO/IPIECA Report Series Volume 2. IPIECA, London, UK. 32pp.

IPIECA (2007) **Guide to Tiered Preparedness and Response**. IPIECA Report Series Volume 14. IPIECA, London, UK. 28pp.

IPIECA (2004) **A Guide to Oiled Wildlife Response Planning**. IPIECA Report Series Volume 13. IPIECA, London, UK. 48pp.

IPIECA (2000) **A Guide to Contingency Planning for Oil Spills on Water**. 2nd edition. IPIECA Report Series Volume 2. IPIECA, London, UK. 28pp.

## Chapter 12: Alternative Techniques

Allen, A., Nabile, N.J., Jaeger, D., Costanzo, D. (2011) **The use of Controlled Burning During the Gulf of Mexico MC-252 Oil Spill Response**. Paper 2011-194 International Oil Spill Conference, 23-26 May 2011, Portland, Oregon, USA. American Petroleum Institute, Washington DC, USA. 13pp.

ARPEL (2006) **A Guide to In-situ Burning of Oil Spills on Water, Shore and Land**. ARPEL Environmental Guidelines 40-2006. ARPEL, Montevideo, Uruguay. 46pp.

IMO (2004) **Bioremediation in Marine Oil Spills**. International Maritime Organization, London, UK. 212pp.

Perring, A.E. et al (2011) **Characteristics of Black Carbon Aerosol from a Surface Oil Burn during the DEEPWATER HORIZON Oil Spill**. Geophysical Research Letters, 38, L17809.

Zhu, X., Venosa, A.D., Suuidan, M.T., Lee, K. (2001) **Guidelines for the Bioremediation of Marine Shorelines and Freshwater Wetlands**. US Environmental Protection Agency Office of Research and Development, Cincinnati, OH, USA. 156pp.

## Technical Information Papers (TIPs)

1. Aerial observation of marine oil spills
2. Fate of marine oil spills
3. Use of booms in oil pollution response
4. Use of dispersants to treat oil spills
5. Use of skimmers in oil pollution response
6. Recognition of oil on shorelines
7. Clean-up of oil from shorelines
8. Use of sorbent materials in oil spill response
9. Disposal of oil and debris
10. Leadership, command and management of oil spills
11. Effects of oil pollution on fisheries and mariculture
12. Effects of oil pollution on social and economic activities
13. Effects of oil pollution on the environment
14. Sampling and monitoring of marine oil spills
15. Preparation and submission of claims from oil pollution
16. Contingency planning for marine oil spills
17. Response to marine chemical incidents

(Also available in Chinese and French)